MATLAB®
&SIMULINK®
STUDENT VERSION

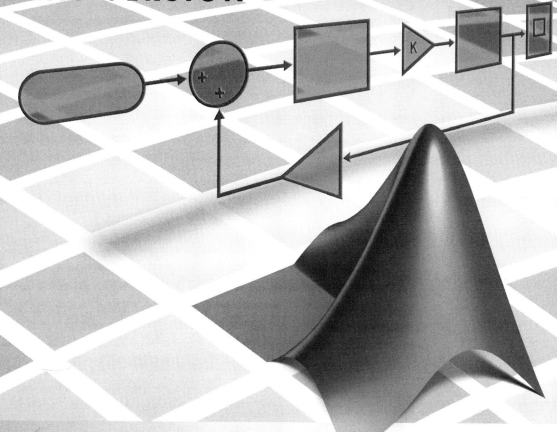

Getting Started with **MATLAB**®

The MathWorks

Accelerating the pace of engineering and science

How to Contact The MathWorks

www.mathworks.com	Web
comp.soft-sys.matlab	Newsgroup
www.mathworks.com/contact_TS.html	Technical Support

suggest@mathworks.com	Product enhancement suggestions
bugs@mathworks.com	Bug reports
doc@mathworks.com	Documentation error reports
service@mathworks.com	Order status, license renewals, passcodes
info@mathworks.com	Sales, pricing, and general information

 508-647-7000 (Phone)

 508-647-7001 (Fax)

The MathWorks, Inc.
3 Apple Hill Drive
Natick, MA 01760-2098

For contact information about worldwide offices, see the MathWorks Web site.

Getting Started with MATLAB

Trademarks

MATLAB, Simulink, Stateflow, Handle Graphics, Real-Time Workshop, and xPC TargetBox are registered trademarks, and SimBiology, SimEvents, and SimHydraulics are trademarks of The MathWorks, Inc.

Other product or brand names are trademarks or registered trademarks of their respective holders.

Patents

The MathWorks products are protected by one or more U.S. patents. Please see www.mathworks.com/patents for more information.

Revision History

December 1996	First printing	For MATLAB 5
May 1997	Second printing	For MATLAB 5.1
September 1998	Third printing	For MATLAB 5.3
September 2000	Fourth printing	Revised for MATLAB 6 (Release 12)
June 2001	Online only	Revised for MATLAB 6.1 (Release 12.1)
July 2002	Online only	Revised for MATLAB 6.5 (Release 13)
August 2002	Fifth printing	Revised for MATLAB 6.5
June 2004	Sixth printing	Revised for MATLAB 7.0 (Release 14)
October 2004	Online only	Revised for MATLAB 7.0.1 (Release 14SP1)
March 2005	Online only	Revised for MATLAB 7.0.4 (Release 14SP2)
June 2005	Seventh printing	Minor revision for MATLAB 7.0.4 (Release 14SP2)
September 2005	Online only	Minor revision for MATLAB 7.1 (Release 14SP3)
March 2006	Online only	Minor revision for MATLAB 7.2 (Release 2006a)
September 2006	Eighth printing	Minor revision for MATLAB 7.3 (Release 2006b)
March 2007	Ninth printing	Minor revision for MATLAB 7.4 (Release 2007a)

Contents

Introduction

1

Matrices and Arrays

2

Graphics

3

Programming

4

Data Analysis

5

Creating Graphical User Interfaces

6

Desktop Tools and Development Environment

7

Index

Introduction

What Is MATLAB?

MATLAB is a high-performance language for technical computing. It integrates computation, visualization, and programming in an easy-to-use environment where problems and solutions are expressed in familiar mathematical notation. Typical uses include

- Math and computation
- Algorithm development
- Data acquisition
- Modeling, simulation, and prototyping
- Data analysis, exploration, and visualization
- Scientific and engineering graphics
- Application development, including graphical user interface building

MATLAB is an interactive system whose basic data element is an array that does not require dimensioning. This allows you to solve many technical computing problems, especially those with matrix and vector formulations, in a fraction of the time it would take to write a program in a scalar noninteractive language such as C or Fortran.

The name MATLAB stands for *matrix laboratory*. MATLAB was originally written to provide easy access to matrix software developed by the LINPACK and EISPACK projects. Today, MATLAB engines incorporate the LAPACK and BLAS libraries, embedding the state of the art in software for matrix computation.

MATLAB has evolved over a period of years with input from many users. In university environments, it is the standard instructional tool for introductory and advanced courses in mathematics, engineering, and science. In industry, MATLAB is the tool of choice for high-productivity research, development, and analysis.

MATLAB features a family of add-on application-specific solutions called *toolboxes*. Very important to most users of MATLAB, toolboxes allow you to *learn* and *apply* specialized technology. Toolboxes are comprehensive collections of MATLAB functions (M-files) that extend the MATLAB environment to solve particular classes of problems. Areas in which toolboxes are available include signal processing, control systems, neural networks, fuzzy logic, wavelets, simulation, and many others.

The MATLAB System

The MATLAB system consists of these main parts:

Desktop Tools and Development Environment

This is the set of tools and facilities that help you use MATLAB functions and files. Many of these tools are graphical user interfaces. It includes the MATLAB desktop and Command Window, a command history, an editor and debugger, a code analyzer and other reports, and browsers for viewing help, the workspace, files, and the search path.

The MATLAB Mathematical Function Library

This is a vast collection of computational algorithms ranging from elementary functions, like sum, sine, cosine, and complex arithmetic, to more sophisticated functions like matrix inverse, matrix eigenvalues, Bessel functions, and fast Fourier transforms.

The MATLAB Language

This is a high-level matrix/array language with control flow statements, functions, data structures, input/output, and object-oriented programming features. It allows both "programming in the small" to rapidly create quick and dirty throw-away programs, and "programming in the large" to create large and complex application programs.

Graphics

MATLAB has extensive facilities for displaying vectors and matrices as graphs, as well as annotating and printing these graphs. It includes high-level functions for two-dimensional and three-dimensional data visualization, image processing, animation, and presentation graphics. It also includes low-level functions that allow you to fully customize the appearance of graphics as well as to build complete graphical user interfaces on your MATLAB applications.

The MATLAB External Interfaces/API

This is a library that allows you to write C and Fortran programs that interact with MATLAB. It includes facilities for calling routines from MATLAB (dynamic linking), calling MATLAB as a computational engine, and for reading and writing MAT-files.

MATLAB Documentation

MATLAB provides extensive documentation, in both printed and online format, to help you learn about and use all of its features. If you are a new user, start with this Getting Started book. It covers all the primary MATLAB features at a high level, including many examples.

The MATLAB online help provides task-oriented and reference information about MATLAB features. MATLAB documentation is also available in printed form and in PDF format.

MATLAB Online Help

To view the online documentation, select **MATLAB Help** from the **Help** menu in MATLAB. The MATLAB documentation is organized into these main topics:

- Desktop Tools and Development Environment — Startup and shutdown, the desktop, and other tools that help you use MATLAB

- Mathematics — Mathematical operations

- Data Analysis — Data analysis, including data fitting, Fourier analysis, and time-series tools

- Programming — The MATLAB language and how to develop MATLAB applications

- Graphics — Tools and techniques for plotting, graph annotation, printing, and programming with Handle Graphics®

- 3-D Visualization — Visualizing surface and volume data, transparency, and viewing and lighting techniques

- Creating Graphical User Interfaces — GUI-building tools and how to write callback functions

- External Interfaces/API — MEX-files, the MATLAB engine, and interfacing to Java, COM, and the serial port

MATLAB also includes reference documentation for all MATLAB functions:

- "Functions — By Category" — Lists all MATLAB functions grouped into categories

- Handle Graphics Property Browser — Provides easy access to descriptions of graphics object properties
- C and Fortran Functions — Covers those functions used by the MATLAB external interfaces, providing information on syntax in the calling language, description, arguments, return values, and examples

The MATLAB online documentation also includes

- Examples — An index of examples included in the documentation
- Release Notes — New features, compatibility considerations, and bug reports
- Printable Documentation — PDF versions of the documentation suitable for printing

In addition to the documentation, you can access demos from the Help browser by clicking the **Demos** tab. Run demos to learn about key functionality of MathWorks products and tools.

For more information about using the Help browser, see "Help for Using MATLAB" in the Desktop Tools and Development Environment documentation.

Starting and Quitting MATLAB

This section explains how to start a new MATLAB session and how to terminate that session when you are finished:

- "Starting MATLAB" on page 1-7
- "Quitting MATLAB" on page 1-8

Starting MATLAB

On Windows platforms, start MATLAB by double-clicking the MATLAB shortcut icon 🐾 on your Windows desktop.

On UNIX platforms, start MATLAB by typing matlab at the operating system prompt.

You can customize MATLAB startup. For example, you can change the directory in which MATLAB starts or automatically execute MATLAB statements in a script file named startup.m.

For More Information See "Starting MATLAB on Windows Platforms" and "Starting MATLAB on UNIX Platforms" in the Desktop Tools and Development Environment documentation.

MATLAB Desktop

When you start MATLAB, the MATLAB desktop appears, containing tools (graphical user interfaces) for managing files, variables, and applications associated with MATLAB.

The following illustration shows the default desktop. You can customize the arrangement of tools and documents to suit your needs. For more information about the desktop tools, see Chapter 7, "Desktop Tools and Development Environment".

Menus change, depending on the tool you are using.

Enter MATLAB statements at the prompt.

View or change the current directory.

Move or resize the Command Window.

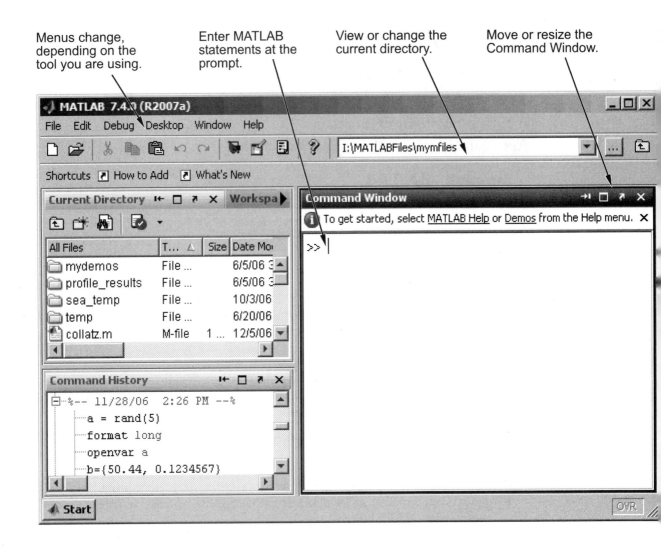

Quitting MATLAB

To end your MATLAB session, select **File > Exit MATLAB** in the desktop, or type quit in the Command Window. You can run a script file named finish.m each time MATLAB quits that, for example, executes functions to save the workspace.

Confirm Quitting

MATLAB can display a confirmation dialog box before quitting. To set this option, select **File > Preferences > General > Confirmation Dialogs**, and select the check box for **Confirm before exiting MATLAB**.

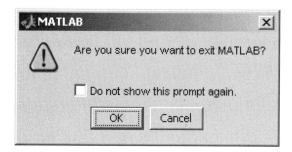

For More Information See "Quitting MATLAB" in the Desktop Tools and Development Environment documentation.

2

Matrices and Arrays

Matrices and Magic Squares

About Matrices

In MATLAB, a matrix is a rectangular array of numbers. Special meaning is sometimes attached to 1-by-1 matrices, which are scalars, and to matrices with only one row or column, which are vectors. MATLAB has other ways of storing both numeric and nonnumeric data, but in the beginning, it is usually best to think of everything as a matrix. The operations in MATLAB are designed to be as natural as possible. Where other programming languages work with numbers one at a time, MATLAB allows you to work with entire matrices quickly and easily. A good example matrix, used throughout this book, appears in the Renaissance engraving Melencolia I by the German artist and amateur mathematician Albrecht Dürer.

This image is filled with mathematical symbolism, and if you look carefully, you will see a matrix in the upper right corner. This matrix is known as a magic square and was believed by many in Dürer's time to have genuinely magical properties. It does turn out to have some fascinating characteristics worth exploring.

Entering Matrices

The best way for you to get started with MATLAB is to learn how to handle matrices. Start MATLAB and follow along with each example.

You can enter matrices into MATLAB in several different ways:

- Enter an explicit list of elements.
- Load matrices from external data files.
- Generate matrices using built-in functions.
- Create matrices with your own functions in M-files.

Start by entering Dürer's matrix as a list of its elements. You only have to follow a few basic conventions:

- Separate the elements of a row with blanks or commas.
- Use a semicolon, ; , to indicate the end of each row.
- Surround the entire list of elements with square brackets, [ ].

To enter Dürer's matrix, simply type in the Command Window

```
A = [16 3 2 13; 5 10 11 8; 9 6 7 12; 4 15 14 1]
```

MATLAB displays the matrix you just entered:

```
A =
    16     3     2    13
     5    10    11     8
     9     6     7    12
     4    15    14     1
```

This matrix matches the numbers in the engraving. Once you have entered the matrix, it is automatically remembered in the MATLAB workspace. You can refer to it simply as A. Now that you have A in the workspace, take a look at what makes it so interesting. Why is it magic?

sum, transpose, and diag

You are probably already aware that the special properties of a magic square have to do with the various ways of summing its elements. If you take the sum along any row or column, or along either of the two main diagonals, you will always get the same number. Let us verify that using MATLAB. The first statement to try is

```
sum(A)
```

MATLAB replies with

```
ans =
    34    34    34    34
```

When you do not specify an output variable, MATLAB uses the variable ans, short for *answer*, to store the results of a calculation. You have computed a row vector containing the sums of the columns of A. Sure enough, each of the columns has the same sum, the *magic* sum, 34.

How about the row sums? MATLAB has a preference for working with the columns of a matrix, so one way to get the row sums is to transpose the matrix, compute the column sums of the transpose, and then transpose the result. For an additional way that avoids the double transpose use the dimension argument for the sum function.

MATLAB has two transpose operators. The apostrophe operator (e.g., A') performs a complex conjugate transposition. It flips a matrix about its main diagonal, and also changes the sign of the imaginary component of any complex elements of the matrix. The apostrophe-dot operator (e.g., A'.), transposes without affecting the sign of complex elements. For matrices containing all real elements, the two operators return the same result.

So

    A'

produces

    ans =
        16   5   9   4
         3   10   6   15
         2   11   7   14
        13   8   12   1

and

    sum(A')'

produces a column vector containing the row sums

    ans =
        34
        34
        34
        34

The sum of the elements on the main diagonal is obtained with the sum and the diag functions:

    diag(A)

produces

    ans =
        16
        10
         7
         1

and

```
sum(diag(A))
```

produces

```
ans =
    34
```

The other diagonal, the so-called *antidiagonal,* is not so important mathematically, so MATLAB does not have a ready-made function for it. But a function originally intended for use in graphics, `fliplr`, flips a matrix from left to right:

```
sum(diag(fliplr(A)))
ans =
    34
```

You have verified that the matrix in Dürer's engraving is indeed a magic square and, in the process, have sampled a few MATLAB matrix operations. The following sections continue to use this matrix to illustrate additional MATLAB capabilities.

Subscripts

The element in row i and column j of A is denoted by A(i,j). For example, A(4,2) is the number in the fourth row and second column. For our magic square, A(4,2) is 15. So to compute the sum of the elements in the fourth column of A, type

```
A(1,4) + A(2,4) + A(3,4) + A(4,4)
```

This produces

```
ans =
    34
```

but is not the most elegant way of summing a single column.

It is also possible to refer to the elements of a matrix with a single subscript, A(k). This is the usual way of referencing row and column vectors. But it can also apply to a fully two-dimensional matrix, in which case the array is regarded as one long column vector formed from the columns of the original matrix. So, for our magic square, A(8) is another way of referring to the value 15 stored in A(4,2).

If you try to use the value of an element outside of the matrix, it is an error:

```
t = A(4,5)
Index exceeds matrix dimensions.
```

On the other hand, if you store a value in an element outside of the matrix, the size increases to accommodate the newcomer:

```
X = A;
X(4,5) = 17

X =
    16     3     2    13     0
     5    10    11     8     0
     9     6     7    12     0
     4    15    14     1    17
```

The Colon Operator

The colon, :, is one of the most important MATLAB operators. It occurs in several different forms. The expression

```
1:10
```

is a row vector containing the integers from 1 to 10:

```
1    2    3    4    5    6    7    8    9    10
```

To obtain nonunit spacing, specify an increment. For example,

```
100:-7:50
```

is

```
100    93    86    79    72    65    58    51
```

and

```
0:pi/4:pi
```

is

```
0     0.7854     1.5708     2.3562     3.1416
```

Subscript expressions involving colons refer to portions of a matrix:

```
A(1:k,j)
```

is the first k elements of the jth column of A. So

```
sum(A(1:4,4))
```

computes the sum of the fourth column. But there is a better way. The colon by itself refers to *all* the elements in a row or column of a matrix and the keyword end refers to the *last* row or column. So

```
sum(A(:,end))
```

computes the sum of the elements in the last column of A:

```
ans =
     34
```

Why is the magic sum for a 4-by-4 square equal to 34? If the integers from 1 to 16 are sorted into four groups with equal sums, that sum must be

```
sum(1:16)/4
```

which, of course, is

```
ans =
     34
```

The magic Function

MATLAB actually has a built-in function that creates magic squares of almost any size. Not surprisingly, this function is named magic:

```
B = magic(4)
B =
    16     2     3    13
     5    11    10     8
     9     7     6    12
     4    14    15     1
```

This matrix is almost the same as the one in the Dürer engraving and has all the same "magic" properties; the only difference is that the two middle columns are exchanged.

To make this B into Dürer's A, swap the two middle columns:

```
A = B(:,[1 3 2 4])
```

This says, for each of the rows of matrix B, reorder the elements in the order 1, 3, 2, 4. It produces

```
A =
    16     3     2    13
     5    10    11     8
     9     6     7    12
     4    15    14     1
```

Why would Dürer go to the trouble of rearranging the columns when he could have used MATLAB ordering? No doubt he wanted to include the date of the engraving, 1514, at the bottom of his magic square.

Expressions

Like most other programming languages, MATLAB provides mathematical *expressions*, but unlike most programming languages, these expressions involve entire matrices. The building blocks of expressions are

- "Variables" on page 2-11
- "Numbers" on page 2-12
- "Operators" on page 2-12
- "Functions" on page 2-13

See also "Examples of Expressions" on page 2-14.

Variables

MATLAB does not require any type declarations or dimension statements. When MATLAB encounters a new variable name, it automatically creates the variable and allocates the appropriate amount of storage. If the variable already exists, MATLAB changes its contents and, if necessary, allocates new storage. For example,

```
num_students = 25
```

creates a 1-by-1 matrix named num_students and stores the value 25 in its single element. To view the matrix assigned to any variable, simply enter the variable name.

Variable names consist of a letter, followed by any number of letters, digits, or underscores. MATLAB is case sensitive; it distinguishes between uppercase and lowercase letters. A and a are *not* the same variable.

Although variable names can be of any length, MATLAB uses only the first N characters of the name, (where N is the number returned by the function namelengthmax), and ignores the rest. Hence, it is important to make each variable name unique in the first N characters to enable MATLAB to distinguish variables.

```
N = namelengthmax
N =
```

63

The genvarname function can be useful in creating variable names that are both valid and unique.

Numbers

MATLAB uses conventional decimal notation, with an optional decimal point and leading plus or minus sign, for numbers. *Scientific notation* uses the letter e to specify a power-of-ten scale factor. *Imaginary numbers* use either i or j as a suffix. Some examples of legal numbers are

```
3              -99           0.0001
9.6397238      1.60210e-20   6.02252e23
1i             -3.14159j     3e5i
```

All numbers are stored internally using the *long* format specified by the IEEE floating-point standard. Floating-point numbers have a finite *precision* of roughly 16 significant decimal digits and a finite *range* of roughly 10^{-308} to 10^{+308}.

Operators

Expressions use familiar arithmetic operators and precedence rules.

+	Addition
-	Subtraction
*	Multiplication
/	Division
\	Left division (described in "Matrices and Linear Algebra" in the MATLAB documentation)
^	Power
'	Complex conjugate transpose
( )	Specify evaluation order

Functions

MATLAB provides a large number of standard elementary mathematical functions, including abs, sqrt, exp, and sin. Taking the square root or logarithm of a negative number is not an error; the appropriate complex result is produced automatically. MATLAB also provides many more advanced mathematical functions, including Bessel and gamma functions. Most of these functions accept complex arguments. For a list of the elementary mathematical functions, type

```
help elfun
```

For a list of more advanced mathematical and matrix functions, type

```
help specfun
help elmat
```

Some of the functions, like sqrt and sin, are *built in*. Built-in functions are part of the MATLAB core so they are very efficient, but the computational details are not readily accessible. Other functions, like gamma and sinh, are implemented in M-files.

There are some differences between built-in functions and other functions. For example, for built-in functions, you cannot see the code. For other functions, you can see the code and even modify it if you want.

Several special functions provide values of useful constants.

pi	3.14159265...
i	Imaginary unit, $\sqrt{-1}$
j	Same as i
eps	Floating-point relative precision, $\varepsilon = 2^{-52}$
realmin	Smallest floating-point number, 2^{-1022}
realmax	Largest floating-point number, $(2-\varepsilon)2^{1023}$
Inf	Infinity
NaN	Not-a-number

Infinity is generated by dividing a nonzero value by zero, or by evaluating well defined mathematical expressions that *overflow*, i.e., exceed `realmax`. Not-a-number is generated by trying to evaluate expressions like 0/0 or `Inf-Inf` that do not have well defined mathematical values.

The function names are not reserved. It is possible to overwrite any of them with a new variable, such as

```
eps = 1.e-6
```

and then use that value in subsequent calculations. The original function can be restored with

```
clear eps
```

Examples of Expressions

You have already seen several examples of MATLAB expressions. Here are a few more examples, and the resulting values:

```
rho = (1+sqrt(5))/2
rho =
    1.6180

a = abs(3+4i)
a =
     5

z = sqrt(besselk(4/3,rho-i))
z =
    0.3730+ 0.3214i

huge = exp(log(realmax))
huge =
  1.7977e+308

toobig = pi*huge
toobig =
    Inf
```

Working with Matrices

This section introduces you to other ways of creating matrices:

- "Generating Matrices" on page 2-15
- "The load Function" on page 2-16
- "M-Files" on page 2-16
- "Concatenation" on page 2-17
- "Deleting Rows and Columns" on page 2-18

Generating Matrices

MATLAB provides four functions that generate basic matrices.

zeros	All zeros
ones	All ones
rand	Uniformly distributed random elements
randn	Normally distributed random elements

Here are some examples:

```
Z = zeros(2,4)
Z =
     0    0    0    0
     0    0    0    0

F = 5*ones(3,3)
F =
     5    5    5
     5    5    5
     5    5    5

N = fix(10*rand(1,10))
N =
     9    2    6    4    8    7    4    0    8    4
```

```
R = randn(4,4)
R =
     0.6353     0.0860    -0.3210    -1.2316
    -0.6014    -2.0046     1.2366     1.0556
     0.5512    -0.4931    -0.6313    -0.1132
    -1.0998     0.4620    -2.3252     0.3792
```

The load Function

The load function reads binary files containing matrices generated by earlier MATLAB sessions, or reads text files containing numeric data. The text file should be organized as a rectangular table of numbers, separated by blanks, with one row per line, and an equal number of elements in each row. For example, outside of MATLAB, create a text file containing these four lines:

```
    16.0     3.0     2.0    13.0
     5.0    10.0    11.0     8.0
     9.0     6.0     7.0    12.0
     4.0    15.0    14.0     1.0
```

Store the file under the name magik.dat. Then the statement

```
load magik.dat
```

reads the file and creates a variable, magik, containing our example matrix.

An easy way to read data into MATLAB in many text or binary formats is to use Import Wizard.

M-Files

You can create your own matrices using *M-files*, which are text files containing MATLAB code. Use the MATLAB Editor or another text editor to create a file containing the same statements you would type at the MATLAB command line. Save the file under a name that ends in .m.

For example, create a file containing these five lines:

```
A = [ ...
    16.0     3.0     2.0    13.0
     5.0    10.0    11.0     8.0
     9.0     6.0     7.0    12.0
```

```
     4.0     15.0     14.0     1.0 ];
```

Store the file under the name magik.m. Then the statement

```
   magik
```

reads the file and creates a variable, A, containing our example matrix.

Concatenation

Concatenation is the process of joining small matrices to make bigger ones. In fact, you made your first matrix by concatenating its individual elements. The pair of square brackets, [ ], is the concatenation operator. For an example, start with the 4-by-4 magic square, A, and form

```
   B = [A  A+32; A+48  A+16]
```

The result is an 8-by-8 matrix, obtained by joining the four submatrices:

```
   B =

      16     3     2    13    48    35    34    45
       5    10    11     8    37    42    43    40
       9     6     7    12    41    38    39    44
       4    15    14     1    36    47    46    33
      64    51    50    61    32    19    18    29
      53    58    59    56    21    26    27    24
      57    54    55    60    25    22    23    28
      52    63    62    49    20    31    30    17
```

This matrix is halfway to being another magic square. Its elements are a rearrangement of the integers 1:64. Its column sums are the correct value for an 8-by-8 magic square:

```
   sum(B)

   ans =
      260   260   260   260   260   260   260   260
```

But its row sums, sum(B')', are not all the same. Further manipulation is necessary to make this a valid 8-by-8 magic square.

Deleting Rows and Columns

You can delete rows and columns from a matrix using just a pair of square brackets. Start with

```
X = A;
```

Then, to delete the second column of X, use

```
X(:,2) = [ ]
```

This changes X to

```
X =
    16     2    13
     5    11     8
     9     7    12
     4    14     1
```

If you delete a single element from a matrix, the result is not a matrix anymore. So, expressions like

```
X(1,2) = [ ]
```

result in an error. However, using a single subscript deletes a single element, or sequence of elements, and reshapes the remaining elements into a row vector. So

```
X(2:2:10) = [ ]
```

results in

```
X =
    16     9     2     7    13    12     1
```

More About Matrices and Arrays

This section explains more about working with matrices and arrays, focusing on

- "Linear Algebra" on page 2-19
- "Arrays" on page 2-23
- "Multivariate Data" on page 2-25
- "Scalar Expansion" on page 2-26
- "Logical Subscripting" on page 2-26
- "The find Function" on page 2-27

Linear Algebra

Informally, the terms *matrix* and *array* are often used interchangeably. More precisely, a *matrix* is a two-dimensional numeric array that represents a *linear transformation*. The mathematical operations defined on matrices are the subject of *linear algebra*.

Dürer's magic square

```
A = [16    3    2   13
      5   10   11    8
      9    6    7   12
      4   15   14    1 ]
```

provides several examples that give a taste of MATLAB matrix operations. You have already seen the matrix transpose, A'. Adding a matrix to its transpose produces a *symmetric* matrix:

```
A + A'

ans =
    32    8   11   17
     8   20   17   23
    11   17   14   26
    17   23   26    2
```

The multiplication symbol, *, denotes the *matrix* multiplication involving inner products between rows and columns. Multiplying the transpose of a matrix by the original matrix also produces a symmetric matrix:

```
A'*A

ans =
    378   212   206   360
    212   370   368   206
    206   368   370   212
    360   206   212   378
```

The determinant of this particular matrix happens to be zero, indicating that the matrix is *singular*:

```
d = det(A)

d =
     0
```

The reduced row echelon form of A is not the identity:

```
R = rref(A)

R =
     1     0     0     1
     0     1     0    -3
     0     0     1     3
     0     0     0     0
```

Since the matrix is singular, it does not have an inverse. If you try to compute the inverse with

```
X = inv(A)
```

you will get a warning message:

```
Warning: Matrix is close to singular or badly scaled.
         Results may be inaccurate. RCOND = 9.796086e-018.
```

Roundoff error has prevented the matrix inversion algorithm from detecting exact singularity. But the value of rcond, which stands for *reciprocal condition estimate*, is on the order of eps, the floating-point relative precision, so the computed inverse is unlikely to be of much use.

The eigenvalues of the magic square are interesting:

```
e = eig(A)

e =
   34.0000
    8.0000
    0.0000
   -8.0000
```

One of the eigenvalues is zero, which is another consequence of singularity. The largest eigenvalue is 34, the magic sum. That is because the vector of all ones is an eigenvector:

```
v = ones(4,1)

v =
     1
     1
     1
     1

A*v

ans =
    34
    34
    34
    34
```

When a magic square is scaled by its magic sum,

```
P = A/34
```

the result is a *doubly stochastic* matrix whose row and column sums are all 1:

```
P =
    0.4706    0.0882    0.0588    0.3824
```

```
0.1471    0.2941    0.3235    0.2353
0.2647    0.1765    0.2059    0.3529
0.1176    0.4412    0.4118    0.0294
```

Such matrices represent the transition probabilities in a *Markov process*. Repeated powers of the matrix represent repeated steps of the process. For our example, the fifth power

```
P^5
```

is

```
0.2507    0.2495    0.2494    0.2504
0.2497    0.2501    0.2502    0.2500
0.2500    0.2498    0.2499    0.2503
0.2496    0.2506    0.2505    0.2493
```

This shows that as k approaches infinity, all the elements in the kth power, P^k, approach 1/4.

Finally, the coefficients in the characteristic polynomial

```
poly(A)
```

are

```
1    -34    -64    2176        0
```

This indicates that the characteristic polynomial

$$\det(A - \lambda I)$$

is

$$\lambda^4 - 34\lambda^3 - 64\lambda^2 + 2176\lambda$$

The constant term is zero, because the matrix is singular, and the coefficient of the cubic term is -34, because the matrix is magic!

Arrays

When they are taken away from the world of linear algebra, matrices become two-dimensional numeric arrays. Arithmetic operations on arrays are done element by element. This means that addition and subtraction are the same for arrays and matrices, but that multiplicative operations are different. MATLAB uses a dot, or decimal point, as part of the notation for multiplicative array operations.

The list of operators includes

+	Addition
-	Subtraction
.*	Element-by-element multiplication
./	Element-by-element division
.\	Element-by-element left division
.^	Element-by-element power
.'	Unconjugated array transpose

If the Dürer magic square is multiplied by itself with array multiplication

```
A.*A
```

the result is an array containing the squares of the integers from 1 to 16, in an unusual order:

```
ans =
    256      9      4    169
     25    100    121     64
     81     36     49    144
     16    225    196      1
```

Building Tables

Array operations are useful for building tables. Suppose n is the column vector

```
n = (0:9)';
```

Then

```
pows = [n  n.^2  2.^n]
```

builds a table of squares and powers of 2:

```
pows =
     0     0     1
     1     1     2
     2     4     4
     3     9     8
     4    16    16
     5    25    32
     6    36    64
     7    49   128
     8    64   256
     9    81   512
```

The elementary math functions operate on arrays element by element. So

```
format short g
x = (1:0.1:2)';
logs = [x log10(x)]
```

builds a table of logarithms.

```
logs =
     1.0           0
     1.1     0.04139
     1.2     0.07918
     1.3     0.11394
     1.4     0.14613
     1.5     0.17609
     1.6     0.20412
     1.7     0.23045
     1.8     0.25527
     1.9     0.27875
     2.0     0.30103
```

Multivariate Data

MATLAB uses column-oriented analysis for multivariate statistical data. Each column in a data set represents a variable and each row an observation. The (i,j)th element is the ith observation of the jth variable.

As an example, consider a data set with three variables:

- Heart rate
- Weight
- Hours of exercise per week

For five observations, the resulting array might look like

```
D = [ 72          134          3.2
      81          201          3.5
      69          156          7.1
      82          148          2.4
      75          170          1.2 ]
```

The first row contains the heart rate, weight, and exercise hours for patient 1, the second row contains the data for patient 2, and so on. Now you can apply many MATLAB data analysis functions to this data set. For example, to obtain the mean and standard deviation of each column, use

```
mu = mean(D), sigma = std(D)

mu =
      75.8         161.8          3.48

sigma =
    5.6303        25.499        2.2107
```

For a list of the data analysis functions available in MATLAB, type

```
help datafun
```

If you have access to Statistics Toolbox, type

```
help stats
```

Scalar Expansion

Matrices and scalars can be combined in several different ways. For example, a scalar is subtracted from a matrix by subtracting it from each element. The average value of the elements in our magic square is 8.5, so

```
B = A - 8.5
```

forms a matrix whose column sums are zero:

```
B =
      7.5      -5.5      -6.5       4.5
     -3.5       1.5       2.5      -0.5
      0.5      -2.5      -1.5       3.5
     -4.5       6.5       5.5      -7.5

sum(B)

ans =
       0         0         0         0
```

With scalar expansion, MATLAB assigns a specified scalar to all indices in a range. For example,

```
B(1:2,2:3) = 0
```

zeroes out a portion of B:

```
B =
      7.5         0         0       4.5
     -3.5         0         0      -0.5
      0.5      -2.5      -1.5       3.5
     -4.5       6.5       5.5      -7.5
```

Logical Subscripting

The logical vectors created from logical and relational operations can be used to reference subarrays. Suppose X is an ordinary matrix and L is a matrix of the same size that is the result of some logical operation. Then X(L) specifies the elements of X where the elements of L are nonzero.

This kind of subscripting can be done in one step by specifying the logical operation as the subscripting expression. Suppose you have the following set of data:

```
x = [2.1 1.7 1.6 1.5 NaN 1.9 1.8 1.5 5.1 1.8 1.4 2.2 1.6 1.8];
```

The NaN is a marker for a missing observation, such as a failure to respond to an item on a questionnaire. To remove the missing data with logical indexing, use isfinite(x), which is true for all finite numerical values and false for NaN and Inf:

```
x = x(isfinite(x))
x =
   2.1 1.7 1.6 1.5 1.9 1.8 1.5 5.1 1.8 1.4 2.2 1.6 1.8
```

Now there is one observation, 5.1, which seems to be very different from the others. It is an *outlier*. The following statement removes outliers, in this case those elements more than three standard deviations from the mean:

```
x = x(abs(x-mean(x)) <= 3*std(x))
x =
   2.1 1.7 1.6 1.5 1.9 1.8 1.5 1.8 1.4 2.2 1.6 1.8
```

For another example, highlight the location of the prime numbers in Dürer's magic square by using logical indexing and scalar expansion to set the nonprimes to 0. (See "The magic Function" on page 2-9.)

```
A(~isprime(A)) = 0

A =
     0     3     2    13
     5     0    11     0
     0     0     7     0
     0     0     0     0
```

The find Function

The find function determines the indices of array elements that meet a given logical condition. In its simplest form, find returns a column vector of indices. Transpose that vector to obtain a row vector of indices. For example, start again with Dürer's magic square. (See "The magic Function" on page 2-9.)

```
k = find(isprime(A))'
```

picks out the locations, using one-dimensional indexing, of the primes in the magic square:

```
k =
     2     5     9    10    11    13
```

Display those primes, as a row vector in the order determined by k, with

```
A(k)
```

```
ans =
     5     3     2    11     7    13
```

When you use k as a left-hand-side index in an assignment statement, the matrix structure is preserved:

```
A(k) = NaN
```

```
A =
    16   NaN   NaN   NaN
   NaN    10   NaN     8
     9     6   NaN    12
     4    15    14     1
```

Controlling Command Window Input and Output

So far, you have been using the MATLAB command line, typing functions and expressions, and seeing the results printed in the Command Window. This section describes

- "The format Function" on page 2-29

- "Suppressing Output" on page 2-30

- "Entering Long Statements" on page 2-31

- "Command Line Editing" on page 2-31

The format Function

The format function controls the numeric format of the values displayed by MATLAB. The function affects only how numbers are displayed, not how MATLAB computes or saves them. Here are the different formats, together with the resulting output produced from a vector x with components of different magnitudes.

Note To ensure proper spacing, use a fixed-width font, such as Courier.

```
x = [4/3 1.2345e-6]

format short

    1.3333     0.0000

format short e

    1.3333e+000   1.2345e-006

format short g

    1.3333   1.2345e-006

format long
```

```
         1.33333333333333    0.00000123450000

format long e

         1.333333333333333e+000    1.234500000000000e-006

format long g

         1.33333333333333                    1.2345e-006

format bank

         1.33            0.00

format rat

         4/3             1/810045

format hex

         3ff5555555555555    3eb4b6231abfd271
```

If the largest element of a matrix is larger than 10^3 or smaller than 10^{-3}, MATLAB applies a common scale factor for the short and long formats.

In addition to the format functions shown above

```
format compact
```

suppresses many of the blank lines that appear in the output. This lets you view more information on a screen or window. If you want more control over the output format, use the sprintf and fprintf functions.

Suppressing Output

If you simply type a statement and press **Return** or **Enter**, MATLAB automatically displays the results on screen. However, if you end the line with a semicolon, MATLAB performs the computation but does not display any output. This is particularly useful when you generate large matrices. For example,

```
A = magic(100);
```

Entering Long Statements

If a statement does not fit on one line, use an ellipsis (three periods), ...,
followed by **Return** or **Enter** to indicate that the statement continues on
the next line. For example,

```
s = 1 -1/2 + 1/3 -1/4 + 1/5 - 1/6 + 1/7 ...
      - 1/8 + 1/9 - 1/10 + 1/11 - 1/12;
```

Blank spaces around the =, +, and - signs are optional, but they improve
readability.

Command Line Editing

Various arrow and control keys on your keyboard allow you to recall, edit,
and reuse statements you have typed earlier. For example, suppose you
mistakenly enter

```
rho = (1 + sqt(5))/2
```

You have misspelled sqrt. MATLAB responds with

```
Undefined function or variable 'sqt'.
```

Instead of retyping the entire line, simply press the ↑ key. The statement
you typed is redisplayed. Use the ← key to move the cursor over and insert
the missing r. Repeated use of the ↑ key recalls earlier lines. Typing a few
characters and then the ↑ key finds a previous line that begins with those
characters. You can also copy previously executed statements from the
Command History. For more information, see "Command History" on page 7-7.

Following is the list of arrow and control keys you can use in the Command
Window. If the preference you select for "Command Window Key Bindings"
is MATLAB standard (Emacs), you can also use the **Ctrl**+key combinations
shown. See also general keyboard shortcuts for desktop tools in the MATLAB
Desktop Tools and Development Environment documentation.

Key	Control Key for MATLAB Standard (Emacs) Preference	Operation
↑	**Ctrl+P**	Recall *previous* line. Works only at command line.
↓	**Ctrl+N**	Recall *next* line. Works only at the prompt if you previously used the up arrow or **Ctrl+P**.
←	**Ctrl+B**	Move *back* one character.
→	**Ctrl+F**	Move *forward* one character.
Ctrl+→	None	Move *right* one word.
Ctrl+←	None	Move *left* one word.
Home	**Ctrl+A**	Move to beginning of current statement.
End	**Ctrl+E**	Move to *end* of current statement.
Ctrl+Home	None	Move to top of Command Window.
Ctrl+End	None	Move to end of Command Window.
Esc	**Ctrl+U**	Clear command line when cursor is at the prompt. Otherwise, move cursor to the prompt.
Delete	**Ctrl+D**	Delete character after cursor.
Backspace	**Ctrl+H**	Delete character before cursor.
None	**Ctrl+K**	Cut contents (*k*ill) to end of command line.
Shift+Home	None	Select from cursor to beginning of statement.
Shift+End	None	Select from cursor to end of statement.

3

Graphics

Overview of MATLAB Plotting

MATLAB provides a wide variety of techniques to display data graphically. Interactive tools enable you to manipulate graphs to achieve results that reveal the most information about your data. You can also annotate and print graphs for presentations, or export graphs to standard graphics formats for presentation in web browsers or other media.

This sections introduces some of the graphics plotting features available with MATLAB:

- "Plotting Process" on page 3-2
- "Graph Components" on page 3-5
- "Figure Tools" on page 3-7
- "Arranging Graphs Within a Figure" on page 3-13
- "Selecting Plot Types" on page 3-14

For More Information MATLAB Graphics and 3-D Visualization in the MATLAB documentation provide in-depth coverage of MATLAB graphics and visualization tools. Access these topics from the Help browser.

Plotting Process

The process of visualizing data typically involves a series of operations. This section provides a "big picture" view of the plotting process and contains links to sections that have examples and specific details about performing each operation.

Creating a Graph

The type of graph you choose to create depends on the nature of your data and what you want to reveal about the data. MATLAB predefines many graph types, such as line, bar, histogram, and pie graphs. There are also 3-D graphs, such as surfaces, slice planes, and streamlines.

There are two basic ways to create graphs in MATLAB:

- Use plotting tools to create graphs interactively.

  See "Some Ways to Use MATLAB Plotting Tools" on page 3-23.

- Use the command interface to enter commands in the Command Window or create plotting programs.

  See "Using Basic Plotting Functions" on page 3-49.

You might find it useful to combine both approaches. For example, you might issue a plotting command to create a graph and then modify the graph using one of the interactive tools.

Exploring Data

Once you create a graph, you can extract specific information about the data, such as the numeric value of a peak in a plot, the average value of a series of data, or you can perform data fitting.

For More Information See "Data Exploration Tools" in the MATLAB Graphics and "Opening the Basic Fitting GUI" in the MATLAB Data Analysis documentation.

Editing the Graph Components

Graphs are composed of objects, which have properties you can change. These properties affect the way the various graph components look and behave.

For example, the axes used to define the coordinate system of the graph has properties that define the limits of each axis, the scale, color, etc. The line used to create a line graph has properties such as color, type of marker used at each data point (if any), line style, etc.

Note that the data used to create a line graph are properties of the line. You can, therefore, change the data without actually creating a new graph.

See "Editing Plots" on page 3-17.

Annotating Graphs

Annotations are the text, arrows, callouts, and other labels added to graphs to help viewers see what is important about the data. You typically add annotations to graphs when you want to show them to other people or when you want to save them for later reference.

For More Information See "Annotating Graphs" in the MATLAB Graphics documentation or select **Annotating Graphs** from the figure **Help** menu.

Printing and Exporting Graphs

You can print your graph on any printer connected to your computer. The print previewer enables you to view how your graph will look when printed. It enables you to add headers, footers, a date, and so on. The print preview dialog lets you control the size, layout, and other characteristics of the graph (select **Print Preview** from the figure **File** menu).

Exporting a graph means creating a copy of it in a standard graphics file format, such as TIF, JPEG, or EPS. You can then import the file into a word processor, include it in an HTML document, or edit it in a drawing package select **Export Setup** from the figure **File** menu).

Adding and Removing Figure Content

By default, when you create a new graph in the same figure window, its data replaces that of the graph that is currently displayed, if any. You can add new data to a graph in several ways; see "Adding More Data to the Graph" on page 3-27 for how to do this using a GUI. You can manually remove all data, graphics and annotations from the current figure by typing CLF in the Command Window or by selecting **Clear Figure** from the figure's **Edit** menu.

For More Information See the print command reference page and "Printing and Exporting" in the MATLAB Graphics documentation or select **Printing and Exporting** from the figure **Help** menu.

Saving Graphs to Reload into MATLAB

There are two ways to save graphs that enable you to save the work you have invested in their preparation:

- Save the graph as a FIG-file (select **Save** from the figure **File** menu).

- Generate MATLAB code that can recreate the graph (select **Generate M-File** from the figure **File** menu).

FIG-Files. FIG-files are a binary format that saves a figure in its current state. This means that all graphics objects and property settings are stored in the file when you create it. You can reload the file into a different MATLAB session, even if you are running MATLAB on a different type of computer. When you load a FIG-file, MATLAB creates a new figure in the same state as the one you saved.

Note that the states of any figure tools (i.e., any items on the toolbars) are not saved in a FIG-file; only the contents of the graph are saved.

Generated Code. You can use the MATLAB M-code generator to create code that recreates the graph. Unlike a FIG-file, the generated code does not contain any data. You must pass appropriate data to the generated function when you run the code.

Studying the generating code for a graph is a good way to learn how to program with MATLAB.

For More Information See the print command reference page and "Saving Your Work" in the MATLAB Graphics documentation.

Graph Components

MATLAB displays graphs in a special window known as a figure. To create a graph, you need to define a coordinate system. Therefore every graph is placed within axes, which are contained by the figure.

The actual visual representation of the data is achieved with graphics objects like lines and surfaces. These objects are drawn within the coordinate system defined by the axes, which MATLAB automatically creates specifically to accommodate the range of the data. The actual data is stored as properties of the graphics objects.

See "Handle Graphics" on page 3-73 for more information about graphics object properties.

The following picture shows the basic components of a typical graph. You can find commands for plotting this graph in "Preparing Graphs for Presentation" on page 3-37.

Figure window displays graphs.

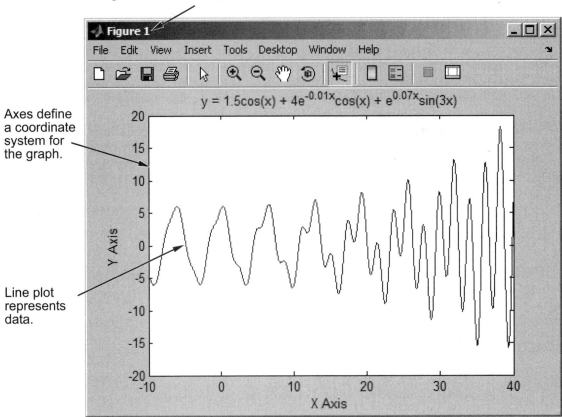

Axes define a coordinate system for the graph.

Line plot represents data.

Figure Tools

The figure is equipped with sets of tools that operate on graphs. The figure **Tools** menu provides access to many graph tools, as this view of the **Options** submenu illustrates. Many of the options shown here are also present as context menu items for individual tools such as zoom and pan. The figure also shows three figure *toolbars*, discussed in "Figure Toolbars" on page 3-8.

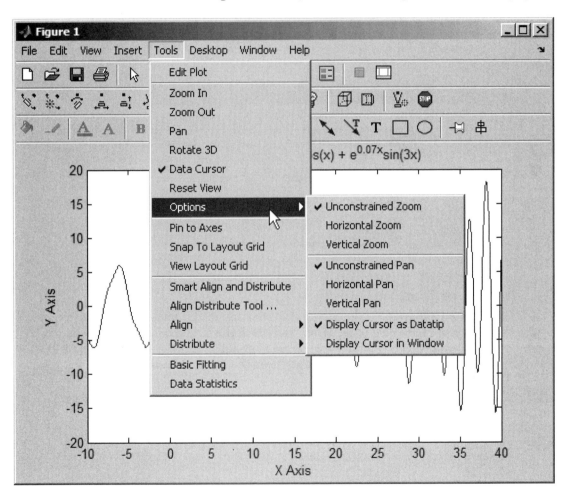

<hr>

For More Information See "Plots and Plotting Tools" in the MATLAB Graphics documentation or select **Plotting Tools** from the figure **Help** menu.

<hr>

Accessing the Tools

You can access or remove the figure toolbars and the plotting tools from the **View** menu, as shown in the following picture. Toggle on and off the toolbars you need. Adding a toolbar stacks it beneath the lowest one.

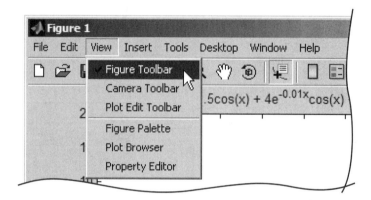

Figure Toolbars

Figure toolbars provide easy access to many graph modification features. There are three toolbars. When you place the cursor over a particular tool, a text box pops up with the tool name. The following picture shows the three toolbars displayed with the cursor over the **Data Cursor** tool.

For More Information See "Anatomy of a Graph" in the MATLAB Graphics documentation.

Plotting Tools

Plotting tools are attached to figures and create an environment for creating graphs. These tools enable you to do the following:

- Select from a wide variety of graph types.

- Change the type of graph that represents a variable.

- See and set the properties of graphics objects.

- Annotate graphs with text, arrows, etc.

- Create and arrange subplots in the figure.

- Drag and drop data into graphs.

Display the plotting tools from the **View** menu or by clicking the **Show Plot Tools** icon in the figure toolbar, as shown in the following picture.

Enable plotting tools from
the View menu or toolbar

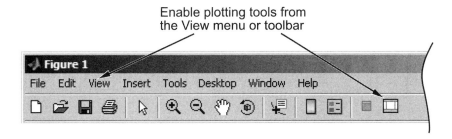

You can also start the plotting tools from the MATLAB prompt:

```
plottools
```

The plotting tools are made up of three independent GUI components:

- Figure Palette — Specify and arrange subplots, access workspace variables for plotting or editing, and add annotations.

- Plot Browser — Select objects in the graphics hierarchy, control visibility, and add data to axes.

- Property Editor — Change key properties of the selected object. Click **More Properties** to access all object properties with the Property Inspector.

You can also control these components from the MATLAB Command Window, by typing the following:

```
figurepalette
plotbrowser
propertyeditor
```

See the reference pages for `plottools`, `figurepalette`, `plotbrowser`, and `propertyeditor` for information on syntax and options.

The following picture shows a figure with all three plotting tools enabled.

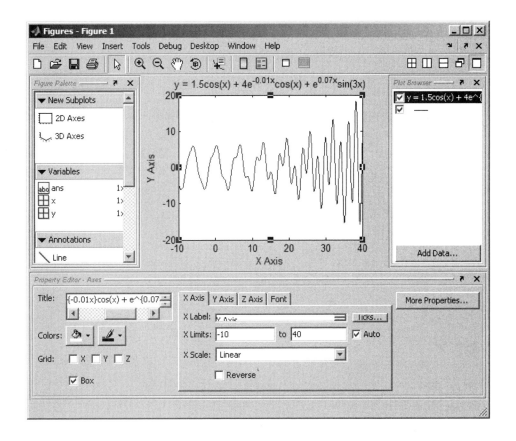

Using Plotting Tools and MATLAB Code

You can enable the plotting tools for any graph, even one created using MATLAB commands. For example, suppose you type the following code to create a graph:

```
t = 0:pi/20:2*pi;
y = exp(sin(t));
plotyy(t,y,t,y,'plot','stem')
xlabel('X Axis')
ylabel('Plot Y Axis')
title('Two Y Axes')
```

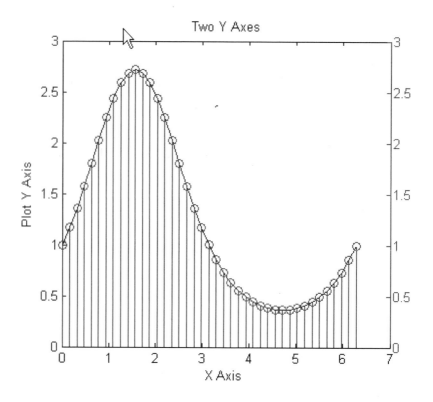

This graph contains two *y*-axes, one for each plot type (a lineseries and a stemseries). The plotting tools make it easy to select any of the objects that the graph contains and modify their properties.

For example, adding a label for the *y*-axis that corresponds to the stem plot is easily accomplished by selecting that axes in the Plot Browser and setting the **Y Label** property in the Property Editor (if you do not see that text field, stretch the Figures window to make it taller).

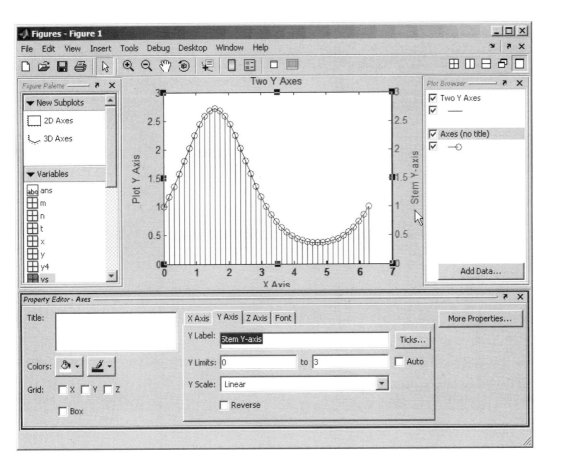

Arranging Graphs Within a Figure

You can place a number of axes within a figure by selecting the layout you want from the Figure Palette. For example, the following picture shows how to specify four 2-D axes in the figure.

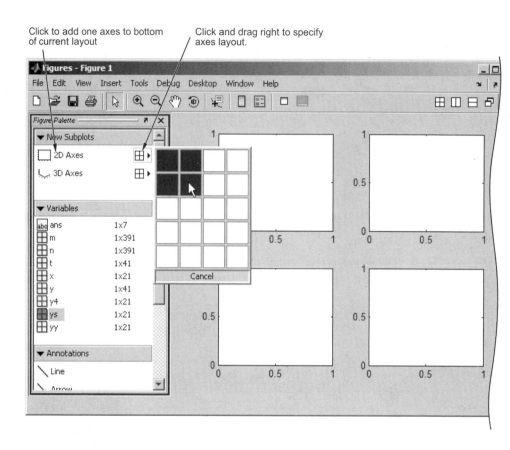

Click to add one axes to bottom of current layout

Click and drag right to specify axes layout.

Select the axes you want to target for plotting. You can also use the subplot function to create multiple axes.

Selecting Plot Types

The types of plots that MATLAB can make are described in "Types of Plots Available in MATLAB" in the MATLAB Graphics documentation. Almost all plots are organized into a tool called the Plot Catalog, which is available from the Figure Palette. You can use the Plot Catalog to choose a plot type for selected variables and then create it in the current figure window. To access the Plot Catalog, select variables and right-click:

1 In the Figure Palette, select the variables you want to plot (first x, and then y, then z).

2 Right-click to display the context menu.

3 Select **More Plots** to display the Plot Catalog.

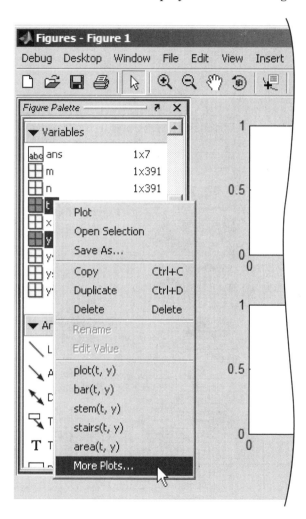

MATLAB displays the Plot Catalog with the selected variables ready to plot, after you select a plot type and click **Plot** or **Plot in New Figure**. You can override the selected variables by typing other variable names or MATLAB expressions in the **Plotted Variables** edit field.

Specify variables to plot.

See a description of each plot type.

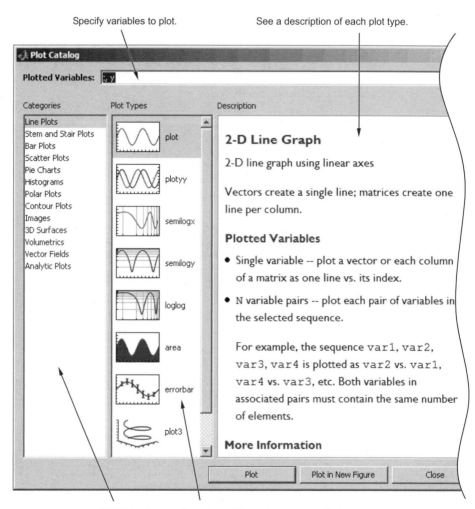

Select a category of graphs and then choose a specific type.

Editing Plots

- "Plot Edit Mode" on page 3-17
- "Using Functions to Edit Graphs" on page 3-22

MATLAB automatically formats graphs by setting the scale of the axes, adding tick marks along axes, and using colors and line styles to distinguish the data plotted in the graph. However, if you are creating graphics for presentation, you can change the default formatting or add descriptive labels, titles, legends and other annotations to help explain your data.

Plot Edit Mode

Plot edit mode lets you select specific objects in a graph and enables you to perform point-and-click editing of most of them.

Enabling Plot Edit Mode

To enable plot edit mode, click the arrowhead in the figure toolbar:

Plot edit mode enabled

You can also select **Edit Plot** from the figure **Tools** menu.

Setting Object Properties

After you have enabled plot edit mode, you can select objects by clicking them in the graph. Selection handles appear and indicate that the object is selected. Select multiple objects using **Shift**+click.

Right-click with the pointer over the selected object to display the object's context menu:

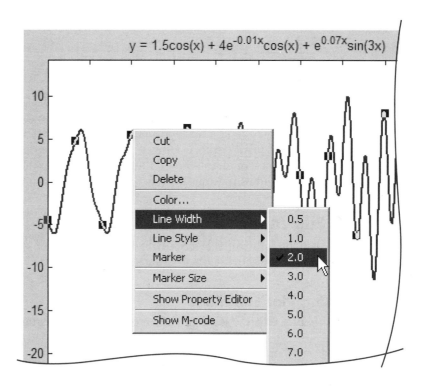

The context menu provides quick access to the most commonly used operations and properties.

Using the Property Editor

In plot edit mode, double-clicking an object in a graph opens the Property Editor GUI with that object's major properties displayed. The Property Editor provides access to the most used object properties. It is updated to display the properties of whatever object you select.

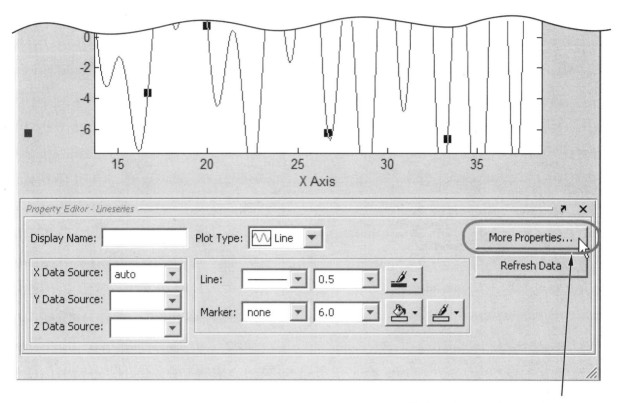

Click to display Property Inspector

Accessing Properties with the Property Inspector

The Property Inspector is a tool that enables you to access most of the properties of Handle Graphics and other MATLAB objects. If you do not find the property you want to set in the Property Editor, click the **More Properties** button to display the Property Inspector. You can also use the inspect command to start the Property Inspector. For example, to inspect the properties of the current axes, type

```
inspect(gca)
```

The following picture shows the Property Inspector displaying the properties of a graph's axes. It lists each property and provides a text field or other appropriate device (such as a color picker) from which you can set the value of the property.

As you select different objects, the Property Inspector is updated to display the properties of the current object.

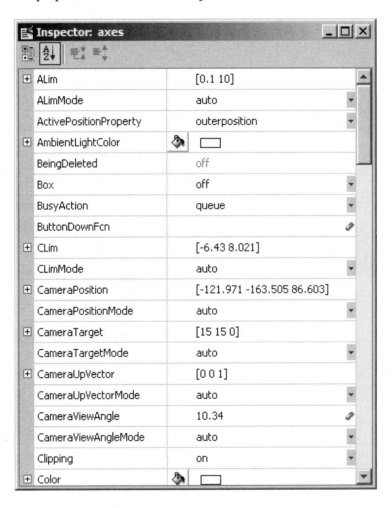

The Property Inspector lists properties alphabetically by default. However, you can group Handle Graphics objects, such as axes, by categories which you can reveal or close in the Property Inspector. To do this, click the 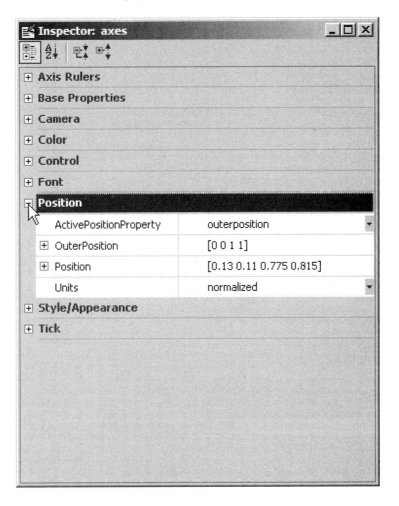 icon at the upper left, then click the + next to the category you want to expand. For example, to see the position-related properties, click the + to the left of the **Position** category.

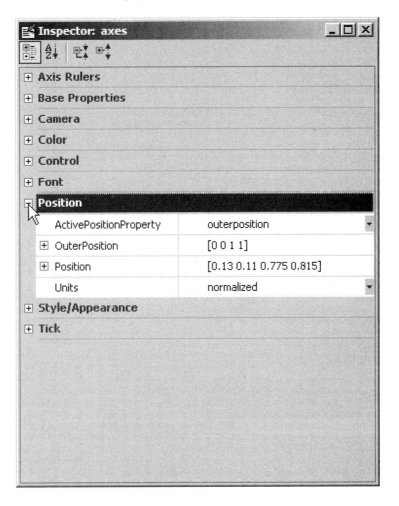

The **Position** category opens and the + changes to a - to indicate that you can collapse the category by clicking it.

Using Functions to Edit Graphs

If you prefer to work from the MATLAB command line, or if you are creating an M-file, you can use MATLAB commands to edit the graphs you create. You can use the set and get commands to change the properties of the objects in a graph. For more information about using graphics commands, see "Handle Graphics" on page 3-73.

Some Ways to Use MATLAB Plotting Tools

- "Plotting Two Variables" on page 3-25
- "Changing the Appearance" on page 3-26
- "Adding More Data to the Graph" on page 3-27
- "Changing the Type of Graph" on page 3-30
- "Modifying the Graph Data Source" on page 3-32

Suppose you want to graph the function $y = x^3$ over the x domain -1 to 1. The first step is to generate the data to plot.

It is simple to evaluate a function because MATLAB can distribute arithmetic operations over all elements of a multivalued variable.

For example, the following statement creates a variable x that contains values ranging from -1 to 1 in increments of 0.1 (you could also use the linspace function to generate data for x). The second statement raises each value in x to the third power and stores these values in y:

```
x = -1:.1:1; % Define the range of x
y = x.^3;    % Raise each element in x to the third power
```

Now that you have generated some data, you can plot it using the MATLAB plotting tools. To start the plotting tools, type

```
plottools
```

MATLAB displays a figure with plotting tools attached.

Variables in workspace   Figure plotting area

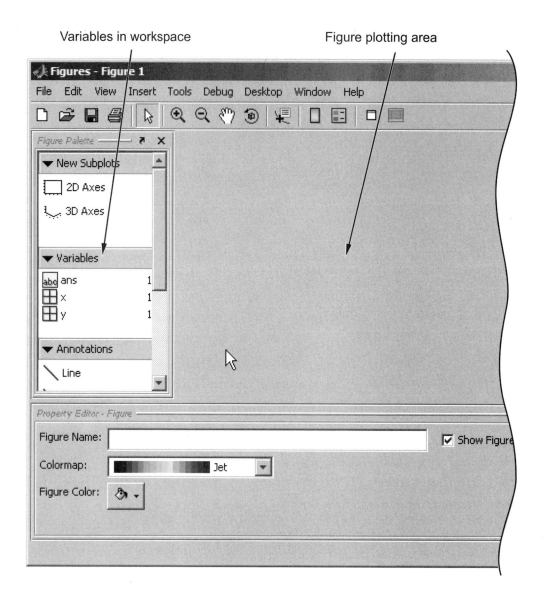

Note When you invoke `plottools`, the set of plotting tools you see and their relative positions depend on how they were configured the last time you used them. Also, sometimes when you dock and undock figures with plotting tools attached, the size or proportions of the various components can change, and you may need to resize one or more of the tool panes.

Plotting Two Variables

A simple line graph is a suitable way to display x as the independent variable and y as the dependent variable. To do this, select both variables (click to select, and then **Shift**+click to select again), and then right-click to display the context menu.

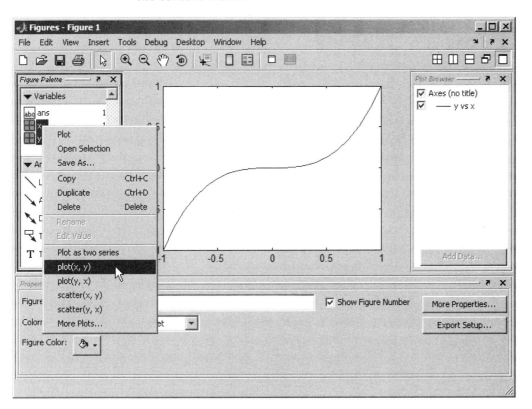

Select **plot(x, y)** from the menu. MATLAB creates the line graph in the figure area. The black squares indicate that the line is selected and you can edit its properties with the Property Editor.

Changing the Appearance

Next change the line properties so that the graph displays only the data point. Use the Property Editor to set following properties:

- Line to no line
- Marker to o (circle)
- Marker size to 4.0
- Marker fill color to red

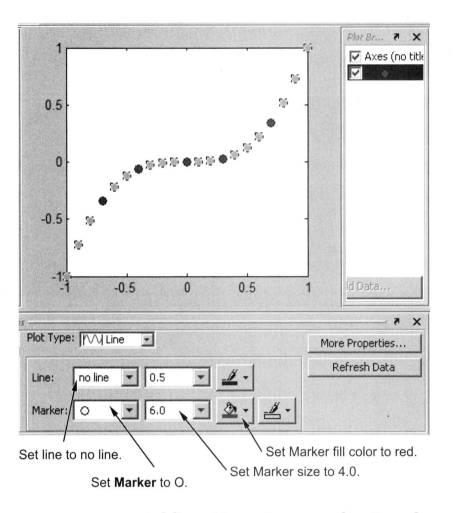

Set line to no line.

Set **Marker** to O.

Set Marker size to 4.0.

Set Marker fill color to red.

Adding More Data to the Graph

You can add more data to the graph by defining more variables or by specifying an expression that MATLAB uses to generate data for the plot. This second approach makes it easy to explore variations of the data already plotted.

To add data to the graph, select the axes in the Plot Browser and click the **Add Data** button. When you are using the plotting tools, MATLAB always adds data to the existing graph, instead of replacing the graph, as it would if you issued repeated plotting commands. That is, the plotting tools are in a hold on state.

To add data using the Plot Browser:

1 Click the **Edit Plot** tool ⌖.

2 Select the axes to which you wish to add data; handles appear around it.

3 Click the **Add Data** button in the Plot Browser; the Add Data to Axes dialog box opens.

4 Select a plot type from the **Plot Type** drop-down menu.

5 Select a variable or type an expression for **X Data Source**.

6 Select a variable or type an expression for **Y Data Source**.

7 Click **OK**; a plot of the data you specified is added to the axes.

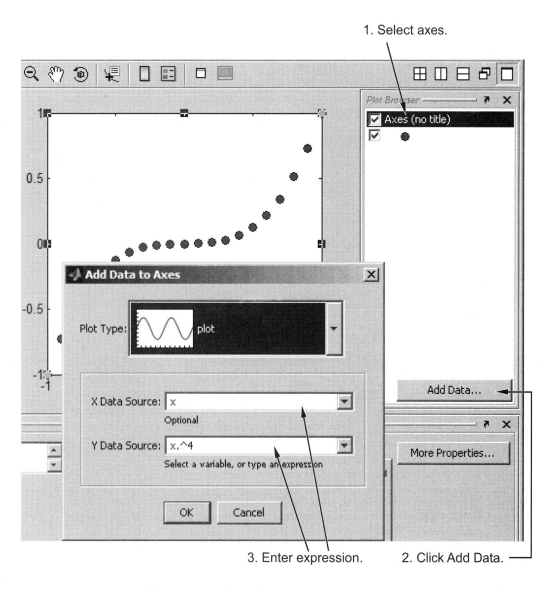

1. Select axes.

2. Click Add Data.

3. Enter expression.

The picture above shows how to use the Add Data to Axes dialog box to create a line plot of $y = x^4$, which is added to the existing plot of $y = x^3$. The resulting plot is shown as follows with the Plot Browser:

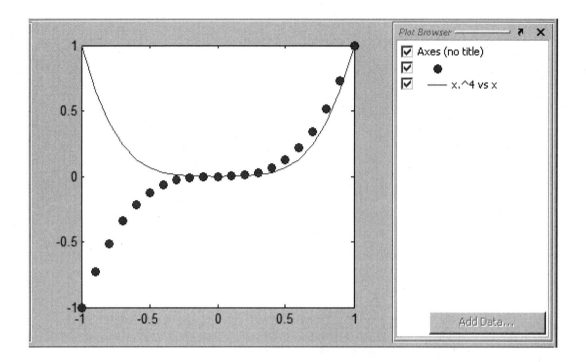

Changing the Type of Graph

The plotting tools enable you to easily view your data with a variety of plot types. The following picture shows the same data as above converted to stem plots. To change the plot type,

1 Select both plotted series in the Plot Browser or **Shift**+click to select them in the plot itself.

2 Select short dashes from the **Line** drop-down menu in the Property Inspector; the line type of both series changes.

3 Select **Stem** from the **Plot Type** menu.

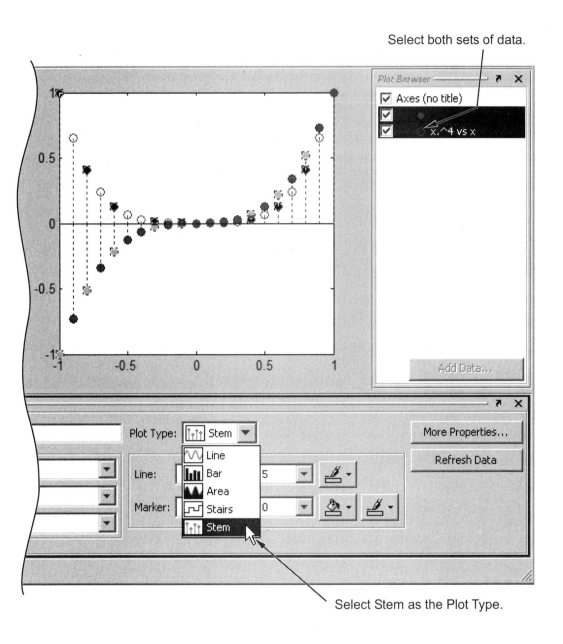

Select both sets of data.

Select Stem as the Plot Type.

Modifying the Graph Data Source

You can link graph data to variables in your workspace. When you change the values contained in the variables, you can then update the graph to use the new data without having to create a new graph. (See also the `refresh` function.)

1 Define 50 points between -3π and 3π and compute their sines and cosines:

```
x = linspace(-3*pi,3*pi,50);
ys = sin(x);
yc = cos(x);
```

2 Using the plotting tools, create a graph of `ys = sin(x)`:

```
figure
plottools
```

3 In the Figure Palette, alternate-click to select x and ys in the **Variable** pane.

4 Right–click either selected variable and choose **plot(x, ys)** from the context menu, as shown below.

The resulting plot looks like this.

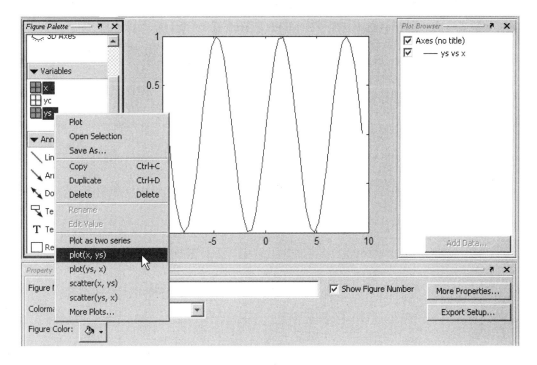

You can use the Property Editor to change the data that this plot displays:

1 Select the line ys vs x in the Plot Browser or by clicking it.

2 In the Property Editor, select yc in the **Y Data Source** drop-down menu.

3 Click the **Refresh Data** button; the plot will change to display a plot of yc vs x.

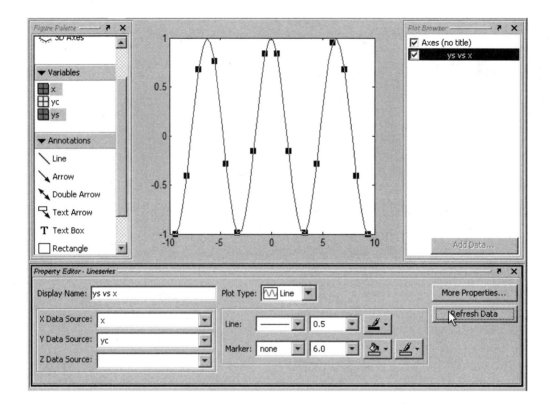

Providing New Values for the Data Source

MATLAB copies the data that defines the graph from variables in the base workspace (for example, x and y) to the XData and YData properties of the plot object (for example, a lineseries). Therefore, in addition to being able to choose new data sources, you can assign new values to workspace variables in the Command Window and click the **Refresh Data** button to update a graph to use the new data.

```
x = linspace(-pi,pi,50); % Define 50 points between -π and π
y = sin(x);
area(x,y)  % Make an area plot of x and y
```

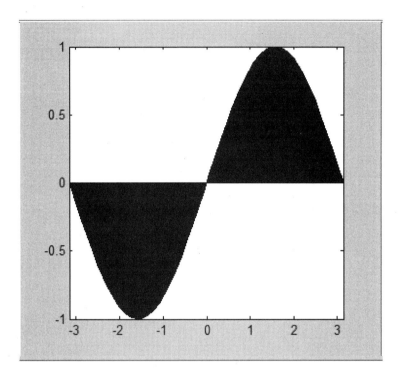

Now recalculate y at the command line:

```
y = cos(x)
```

Select the blue line on the plot. Select, x as the **X Data Source**, y as the **Y Data Source**, and click **Refresh Data**. The graph's XData and YData are replaced, making the plot look like this.

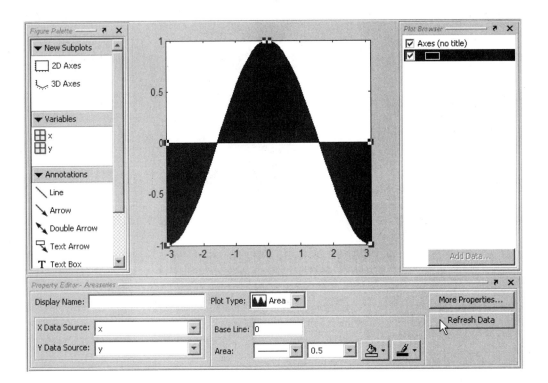

Preparing Graphs for Presentation

- "Modifying the Graph to Enhance the Presentation" on page 3-38
- "Printing the Graph" on page 3-42
- "Exporting the Graph" on page 3-46

Suppose you plot the following data and want to create a graph that presents certain information about the data:

```
x = -10:.005:40;
y = [1.5*cos(x)+4*exp(-.01*x).*cos(x)+exp(.07*x).*sin(3*x)];
plot(x,y)
```

This picture shows the graph created by the previous code.

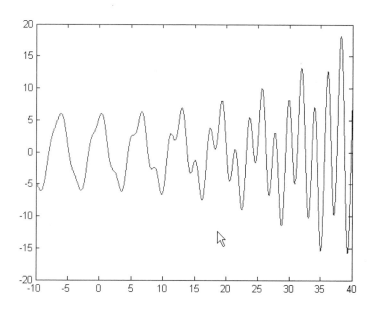

Now suppose you want to save copies of the graph by

- Printing the graph on a local printer so you have a copy for your notebook

- Exporting the graph to an Encapsulated PostScript (EPS) file to incorporate into a word processor document

Modifying the Graph to Enhance the Presentation

To obtain a better view, zoom in on the graph using horizontal zoom.

Enable zoom mode by clicking the **Zoom** tool on the figure toolbar, and then right-click to display the context menu. Select **Horizontal Zoom (2-D Plots Only)** from **Zoom Options**. Notice that you can reverse your zoom direction by **Shift**-left-clicking, or using the context menu.

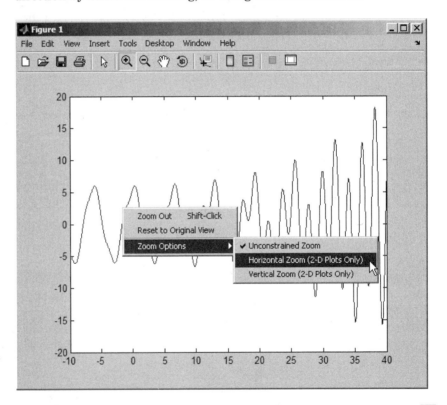

Left-click to zoom in on a region of the graph and use the **Pan** tool to position the points of interest where you want them on the graph.

Label some key points with data tips using the **Data Cursor** tool ![icon]. Notice that left-clicking the line moves the last datatip you created to where you just clicked. To create a new datatip, press **Alt**+click or use the tool's context menu. See "Data Cursor — Displaying Data Values Interactively" in the MATLAB Graphics documentation for more information on using datatips.

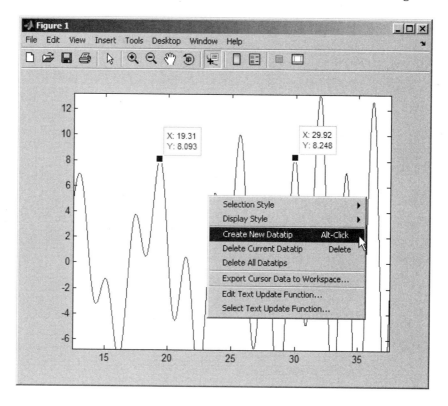

Next use the Figure Palette to annotate the plot. Choose the Double arrow tool in the Annotations section to draw a line between two datatips, as shown below:

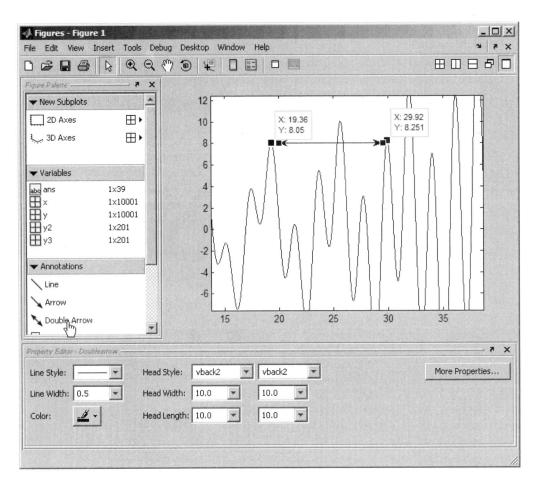

Now add a text box, also using the Figure Palette. You may have to scroll to see the text box icon. Drag out a box, and then type into it. You can stretch or shrink the box with its handles, and center the text with the Property Editor while the text box is selected. You can also use the Property Editor to change the text font, size, style, and color, as well as the text box line and background colors.

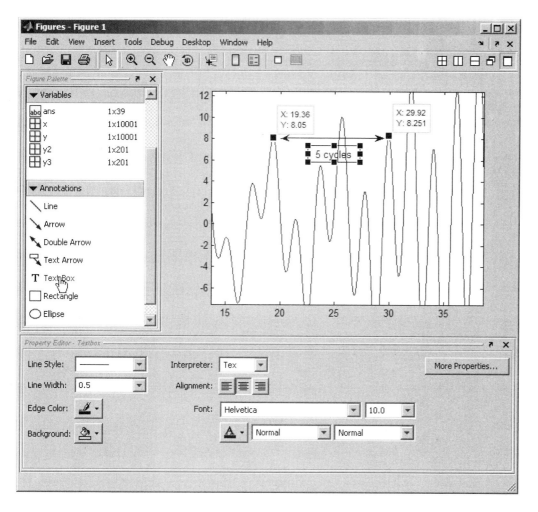

Finally, add text annotations, axis labels, and a title. You can add the title and axis labels using the following commands:

```
title ('y = 1.5cos(x) + 4e^{-0.01x}cos(x) + e^{0.07x}sin(3x)')
xlabel('X Axis')
ylabel('Y Axis')
```

Note that the text string passed to the `title` command uses T_EX syntax to produce the exponents. See "Information About Using T_EX" in the Text

Properties page in the MATLAB Function Reference documentation about using T_EX syntax to produce mathematical symbols.

You can also add these annotations by selecting the axes and typing the above strings into their respective fields in the Property Editor. The graph is now ready to print and export.

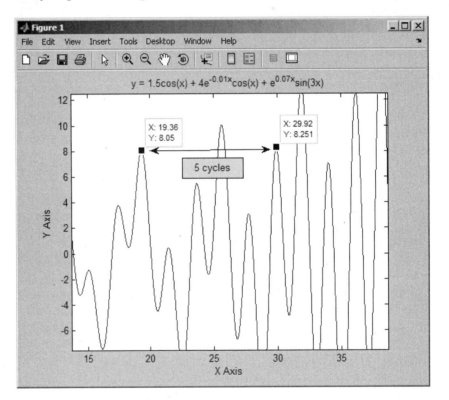

Printing the Graph

Before printing the graph, use the print previewer to see and modify how the graph will be laid out on the page. Select **Print Preview** from the figure **File** menu. The Print Preview window opens, containing a tabbed control panel on its left side and a page image on its right side.

- Click the **Lines/Text** tab, and enter a line of text in the **Header Text** edit field that you want to place at the top of the page. You can change the font, style, and size of the header by clicking the **Font** button beneath the text field, and also use the **Date Style** drop-down list to specify a date format to add the current date/time to the header.

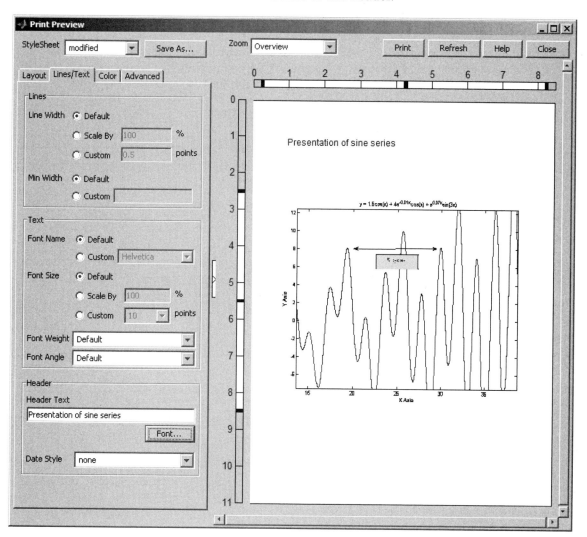

- Notice the three black handlebars in the rulers along the left and top sides of the preview pane. The outside handlebars let you stretch one edge of the plot, leaving the other edges in place. The inner handlebars let you move the plot up and down or left and right without stretching it. Using them does not affect the figure itself, only the printed version of it.

- You can also change the size and position of the plot on the page using the buttons and edit boxes on the **Layout** tab. You can revert to the original configuration by clicking the **Auto (Actual Size, Centered)** option button, and correct stretching and shrinking by clicking **Fix Aspect Ratio**. The following picture shows the **Layout** tab in Auto configuration.

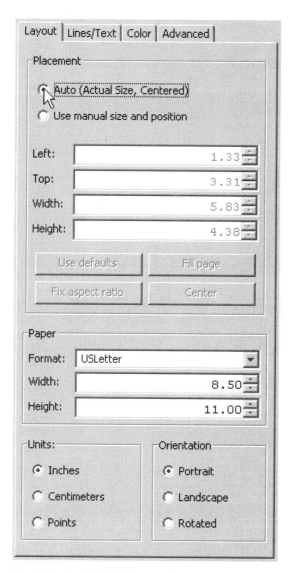

- By default, MATLAB recalculates the locations of the axes tick marks because a printed graph is normally larger than the one displayed on your monitor. However, you can keep your graph's tick marks and limits when printing it by clicking the **Advanced** tab and selecting **Keep screen limits and ticks**.

- When you are ready to print your plot, click **Print** in the right pane. You can also click **Close** to accept the settings and dismiss the dialog box. Later, you can print the figure as you previewed it using **Print** on the figure's **File** menu. Both methods will open a standard Print dialog box, and will produce the same printed results.

Note There is no way to cancel a print preview; any changes you make will take effect if you print the figure. If you want to revert to a default page layout, you can generally accomplish this by selecting either the **Use Defaults** button or the **Auto (Actual Size, Centered)** option button on the **Layout** tab, although this will not affect every setting you can make.

The Print Preview dialog box provides many other options for controlling how printed graphs look. Click its **Help** button for more information.

Exporting the Graph

Exporting a graph is the process of creating a standard graphics file format of the graph (such as EPS or TIFF), which you can then import into other applications like word processors, drawing packages, etc.

This example exports the graph as an EPS file with the following requirements:

- The size of the picture when imported into the word processor document should be 4 inches wide and 3 inches high.

- All the text in the figure should have a size of 8 points.

Specifying the Size of the Graph

To set the size, use the Export Setup dialog box (select **Export Setup** from the figure **File** menu). Then select 4 from the **Width** list and 3 from the **Height** list.

Set the size at which to
export the graph to a file.

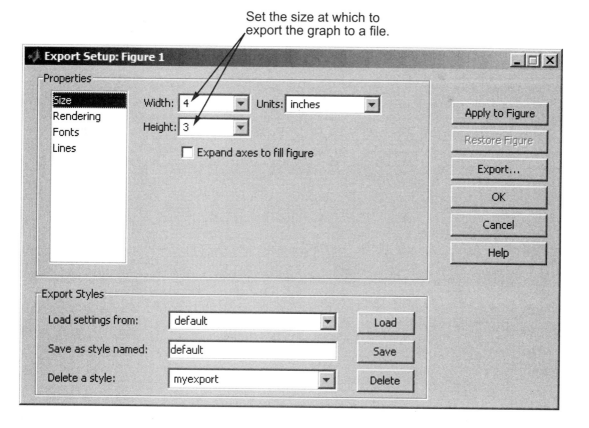

Specifying the Font Size

To set the font size of all the text in the graph, select Fonts in the Export
Setup dialog box **Properties** selector. Then click **Use fixed font size** and
enter 8 in the text box.

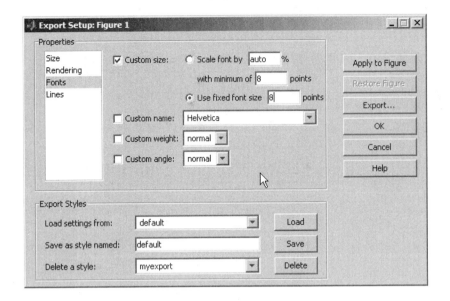

Selecting the File Format

After you finish setting options for the exported graph, click the **Export** button. MATLAB displays a standard Save As dialog box that enables you to specify a name for the file as well as select the type of file format you want to use.

The **Save as type** drop-down menu lists a number of other options for file formats. For this example, select EPS (*.eps) from the **Save as type** menu.

You can import the saved file into any application that supports EPS files.

You can also use the print command to print figures on your local printer or to export graphs to standard file types.

For More Information See the print command reference page and "Printing and Exporting" in the MATLAB Graphics documentation or select **Printing and Exporting** from the figure **Help** menu.

Using Basic Plotting Functions

This section describes important graphics functions and provides examples of some typical applications. The plotting tools, described in "Some Ways to Use MATLAB Plotting Tools" on page 3-23, use MATLAB plotting functions to create graphs interactively and can generate code for graphs they create:

- "Creating a Plot" on page 3-49
- "Plotting Multiple Data Sets in One Graph" on page 3-50
- "Specifying Line Styles and Colors" on page 3-51
- "Plotting Lines and Markers" on page 3-52
- "Graphing Imaginary and Complex Data" on page 3-53
- "Adding Plots to an Existing Graph" on page 3-54
- "Figure Windows" on page 3-55
- "Displaying Multiple Plots in One Figure" on page 3-56
- "Controlling the Axes" on page 3-58
- "Adding Axis Labels and Titles" on page 3-59
- "Saving Figures" on page 3-61

Creating a Plot

The plot function has different forms, depending on the input arguments. If y is a vector, plot(y) produces a piecewise linear graph of the elements of y versus the index of the elements of y. If you specify two vectors as arguments, plot(x,y) produces a graph of y versus x.

For example, these statements use the colon operator to create a vector of x values ranging from 0 to 2π, compute the sine of these values, and plot the result:

```
x = 0:pi/100:2*pi;
y = sin(x);
plot(x,y)
```

Now label the axes and add a title. The characters \pi create the symbol π. See "text strings" in the MATLAB Reference documentation for more symbols:

```
xlabel('x = 0:2\pi')
ylabel('Sine of x')
title('Plot of the Sine Function','FontSize',12)
```

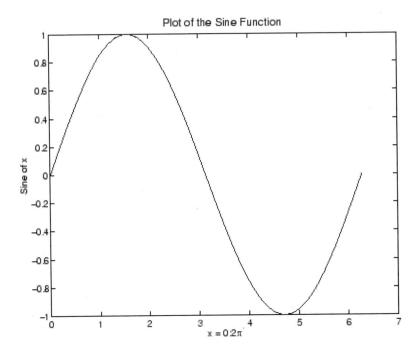

Plotting Multiple Data Sets in One Graph

Multiple x-y pair arguments create multiple graphs with a single call to plot. MATLAB automatically cycles through a predefined (but user settable) list of colors to allow discrimination among sets of data. See the axes ColorOrder and LineStyleOrder properties.

For example, these statements plot three related functions of x, with each curve in a separate distinguishing color:

```
x = 0:pi/100:2*pi;
y = sin(x);
y2 = sin(x-.25);
y3 = sin(x-.5);
plot(x,y,x,y2,x,y3)
```

The `legend` command provides an easy way to identify the individual plots:

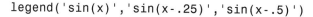

```
legend('sin(x)','sin(x-.25)','sin(x-.5)')
```

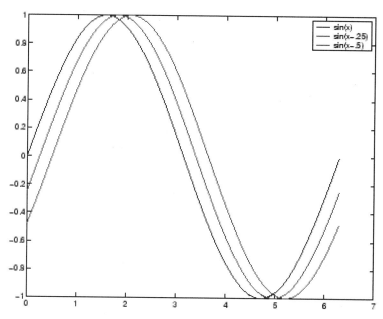

For More Information See "Defining the Color of Lines for Plotting" in the MATLAB Graphics documentation.

Specifying Line Styles and Colors

It is possible to specify color, line styles, and markers (such as plus signs or circles) when you plot your data using the `plot` command:

```
plot(x,y,'color_style_marker')
```

color_style_marker is a string containing from one to four characters (enclosed in single quotation marks) constructed from a color, a line style, and a marker type:

- Color strings are `'c'`, `'m'`, `'y'`, `'r'`, `'g'`, `'b'`, `'w'`, and `'k'`. These correspond to cyan, magenta, yellow, red, green, blue, white, and black.

- Line style strings are `-` for solid, `--` for dashed, `:` for dotted, and `-.` for dash-dot. Omit the line style for no line.

- The marker types are `+`, `o`, `*`, and `x`, and the filled marker types are `s` for square, `d` for diamond, `^` for up triangle, `v` for down triangle, `>` for right triangle, `<` for left triangle, `p` for pentagram, `h` for hexagram, and none for no marker.

You can also edit color, line style, and markers interactively. See "Editing Plots" on page 3-17 for more information.

Plotting Lines and Markers

If you specify a marker type but not a line style, MATLAB draws only the marker. For example,

```
plot(x,y,'ks')
```

plots black squares at each data point, but does not connect the markers with a line.

The statement

```
plot(x,y,'r:+')
```

plots a red dotted line and places plus sign markers at each data point.

Placing Markers at Every Tenth Data Point

You might want to use fewer data points to plot the markers than you use to plot the lines. This example plots the data twice using a different number of points for the dotted line and marker plots:

```
x1 = 0:pi/100:2*pi;
x2 = 0:pi/10:2*pi;
plot(x1,sin(x1),'r:',x2,sin(x2),'r+')
```

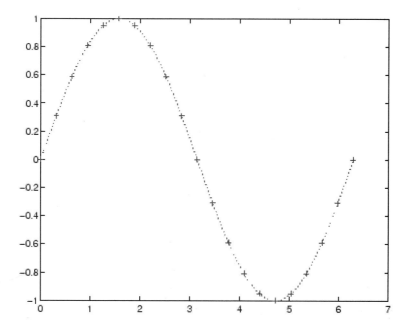

Graphing Imaginary and Complex Data

When the arguments to plot are complex, the imaginary part is ignored *except* when you pass plot a single complex argument. For this special case, the command is a shortcut for a graph of the real part versus the imaginary part. Therefore,

```
plot(Z)
```

where Z is a complex vector or matrix, is equivalent to

```
plot(real(Z),imag(Z))
```

For example,

```
t = 0:pi/10:2*pi;
plot(exp(i*t),'-o')
axis equal
```

draws a 20-sided polygon with little circles at the vertices. The axis equal command makes the individual tick-mark increments on the *x*- and *y*-axes the same length, which makes this plot more circular in appearance.

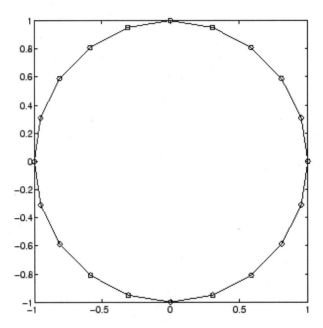

Adding Plots to an Existing Graph

The hold command enables you to add plots to an existing graph. When you type

```
hold on
```

MATLAB does not replace the existing graph when you issue another plotting command; it adds the new data to the current graph, rescaling the axes if necessary.

For example, these statements first create a contour plot of the peaks function, then superimpose a pseudocolor plot of the same function:

```
[x,y,z] = peaks;
pcolor(x,y,z)
shading interp
```

```
hold on
contour(x,y,z,20,'k')
hold off
```

The hold on command combines the pcolor plot with the contour plot in one figure.

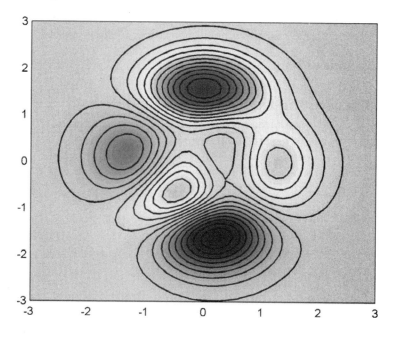

_____

For More Information See "Creating Specialized Plots" in the MATLAB Graphics documentation for details about a variety of graph types.

_____

Figure Windows

Graphing functions automatically open a new figure window if there are no figure windows already on the screen. If a figure window exists, MATLAB uses that window for graphics output. If there are multiple figure windows open, MATLAB targets the one that is designated the "current figure" (the last figure used or clicked in).

To make an existing figure window the current figure, you can click the mouse while the pointer is in that window or you can type

```
figure(n)
```

where n is the number in the figure title bar. The results of subsequent graphics commands are displayed in this window.

To open a new figure window and make it the current figure, type

```
figure
```

Clearing the Figure for a New Plot

When a figure already exists, most plotting commands clear the axes and use this figure to create the new plot. However, these commands do not reset figure properties, such as the background color or the colormap. If you have set any figure properties in the previous plot, you might want to use the clf command with the reset option,

```
clf reset
```

before creating your new plot to restore the figure's properties to their defaults.

For More Information See "Figure Properties" and "Graphics Windows — the Figure" in the MATLAB Graphics documentation for details about figures.

Displaying Multiple Plots in One Figure

The subplot command enables you to display multiple plots in the same window or print them on the same piece of paper. Typing

```
subplot(m,n,p)
```

partitions the figure window into an m-by-n matrix of small subplots and selects the pth subplot for the current plot. The plots are numbered along the first row of the figure window, then the second row, and so on. For example, these statements plot data in four different subregions of the figure window:

```
t = 0:pi/10:2*pi;
```

```
[X,Y,Z] = cylinder(4*cos(t));
subplot(2,2,1); mesh(X)
subplot(2,2,2); mesh(Y)
subplot(2,2,3); mesh(Z)
subplot(2,2,4); mesh(X,Y,Z)
```

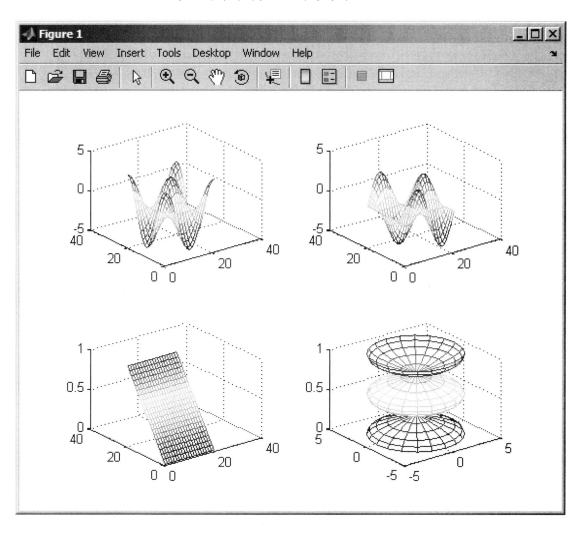

You can add subplots to GUIs as well as to figures. For details about creating subplots in a GUIDE-generated GUI, see "Creating Subplots" in the MATLAB Creating Graphical User Interfaces documentation.

Controlling the Axes

The axis command provides a number of options for setting the scaling, orientation, and aspect ratio of graphs. You can also set these options interactively. See "Editing Plots" on page 3-17 for more information.

Setting Axis Limits

By default, MATLAB finds the maxima and minima of the data and chooses the axis limits to span this range. The axis command enables you to specify your own limits:

```
axis([xmin xmax ymin ymax])
```

or for three-dimensional graphs,

```
axis([xmin xmax ymin ymax zmin zmax])
```

Use the command

```
axis auto
```

to reenable MATLAB automatic limit selection.

Setting the Axis Aspect Ratio

The axis command also enables you to specify a number of predefined modes. For example,

```
axis square
```

makes the x-axis and y-axis the same length.

```
axis equal
```

makes the individual tick mark increments on the x-axes and y-axes the same length. This means

```
plot(exp(i*[0:pi/10:2*pi]))
```

followed by either `axis square` or `axis equal` turns the oval into a proper circle:

```
axis auto normal
```

returns the axis scaling to its default automatic mode.

Setting Axis Visibility

You can use the `axis` command to make the axis visible or invisible.

```
axis on
```

makes the axes visible. This is the default.

```
axis off
```

makes the axes invisible.

Setting Grid Lines

The `grid` command toggles grid lines on and off. The statement

```
grid on
```

turns the grid lines on, and

```
grid off
```

turns them back off again.

For More Information See the `axis` and `axes` reference pages and "Axes Properties" in the MATLAB Graphics documentation.

Adding Axis Labels and Titles

The `xlabel`, `ylabel`, and `zlabel` commands add x-, y-, and z-axis labels. The `title` command adds a title at the top of the figure and the `text` function inserts text anywhere in the figure.

You can produce mathematical symbols using LaTeX notation in the text string, as the following example illustrates:

```
t = -pi:pi/100:pi;
y = sin(t);
plot(t,y)
axis([-pi pi -1 1])
xlabel('-\pi \leq {\itt} \leq \pi')
ylabel('sin(t)')
title('Graph of the sine function')
text(1,-1/3,'{\itNote the odd symmetry.}')
```

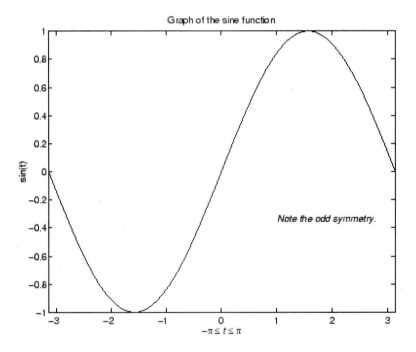

You can also set these options interactively. See "Editing Plots" on page 3-17 for more information.

Note that the location of the text string is defined in axes units (i.e., the same units as the data). See the annotation function for a way to place text in normalized figure units.

Saving Figures

Save a figure by selecting **Save** from the **File** menu to display a Save dialog box. MATLAB saves the data it needs to recreate the figure and its contents (i.e., the entire graph) in a file with a `.fig` extension.

To save a figure using a standard graphics format, such as TIFF, for use with other applications, select **Export Setup** from the **File** menu. You can also save from the command line—use the `saveas` command, including any options to save the figure in a different format. The more restricted `hgexport` command, which saves figures to either bitmap or metafile files, depending on the rendering method in effect, is also available.

See "Exporting the Graph" on page 3-46 for an example.

Saving Workspace Data

You can save the variables in your workspace by selecting **Save Workspace As** from the figure **File** menu. You can reload saved data using the **Import Data** item in the figure **File** menu. MATLAB supports a variety of data file formats, including MATLAB data files, which have a `.mat` extension.

Generating M-Code to Recreate a Figure

You can generate MATLAB code that recreates a figure and the graph it contains by selecting **Generate M-File** from the figure **File** menu. This option is particularly useful if you have developed a graph using plotting tools and want to create a similar graph using the same or different data.

Saving Figures That Are Compatible with the Previous Version of MATLAB

Create backward-compatible FIG-files by following these two steps:

1 Ensure that any plotting functions used to create the contents of the figure are called with the `'v6'` argument, where applicable.

2 Use the `'-v6'` option with the `hgsave` command.

For More Information See "Plot Objects and Backward Compatibility" in the MATLAB Graphics documentation.

Creating Mesh and Surface Plots

MATLAB defines a surface by the z-coordinates of points above a grid in the x-y plane, using straight lines to connect adjacent points. The mesh and surf plotting functions display surfaces in three dimensions. mesh produces wireframe surfaces that color only the lines connecting the defining points. surf displays both the connecting lines and the faces of the surface in color.

The figure colormap and figure properties determine how MATLAB colors the surface.

Visualizing Functions of Two Variables

To display a function of two variables, $z = f(x,y)$,

1 Generate X and Y matrices consisting of repeated rows and columns, respectively, over the domain of the function.

2 Use X and Y to evaluate and graph the function.

The meshgrid function transforms the domain specified by a single vector or two vectors x and y into matrices X and Y for use in evaluating functions of two variables. The rows of X are copies of the vector x and the columns of Y are copies of the vector y.

Example — Graphing the sinc Function

This example evaluates and graphs the two-dimensional sinc function, $\sin(r)/r$, between the x and y directions. R is the distance from the origin, which is at the center of the matrix. Adding eps (a MATLAB command that returns a small floating-point number) avoids the indeterminate 0/0 at the origin:

```
[X,Y] = meshgrid(-8:.5:8);
R = sqrt(X.^2 + Y.^2) + eps;
Z = sin(R)./R;
mesh(X,Y,Z,'EdgeColor','black')
```

3-63

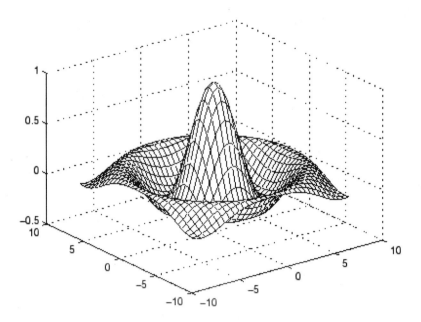

By default, MATLAB colors the mesh using the current colormap. However, this example uses a single-colored mesh by specifying the EdgeColor surface property. See the surface reference page for a list of all surface properties.

You can create a mesh with see-through faces by disabling hidden line removal:

```
hidden off
```

See the hidden reference page for more information on this option.

Example — Colored Surface Plots

A surface plot is similar to a mesh plot except that MATLAB colors the rectangular faces of the surface. The color of each face is determined by the values of Z and the colormap (a colormap is an ordered list of colors). These statements graph the sinc function as a surface plot, specify a colormap, and add a color bar to show the mapping of data to color:

```
surf(X,Y,Z)
colormap hsv
colorbar
```

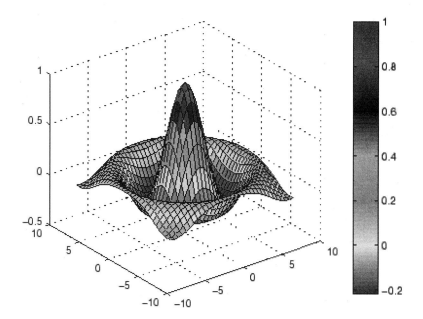

See the colormap reference page for information on colormaps.

For More Information See "Creating 3-D Graphs" in the MATLAB 3-D
Visualization documentation for more information on surface plots.

Making Surfaces Transparent

You can make the faces of a surface transparent to a varying degree.
Transparency (referred to as the alpha value) can be specified for the whole
object or can be based on an alphamap, which behaves similarly to colormaps.
For example,

```
surf(X,Y,Z)
colormap hsv
alpha(.4)
```

produces a surface with a face alpha value of 0.4. Alpha values range from 0
(completely transparent) to 1 (not transparent).

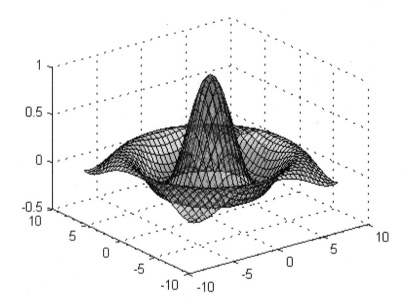

For More Information See "Transparency" in the MATLAB 3-D
Visualization documentation for details about using this feature.

Illuminating Surface Plots with Lights

Lighting is the technique of illuminating an object with a directional light
source. In certain cases, this technique can make subtle differences in
surface shape easier to see. Lighting can also be used to add realism to
three-dimensional graphs.

This example uses the same surface as the previous examples, but colors it
red and removes the mesh lines. A light object is then added to the left of the
"camera" (the camera is the location in space from where you are viewing
the surface):

```
surf(X,Y,Z,'FaceColor','red','EdgeColor','none')
camlight left; lighting phong
```

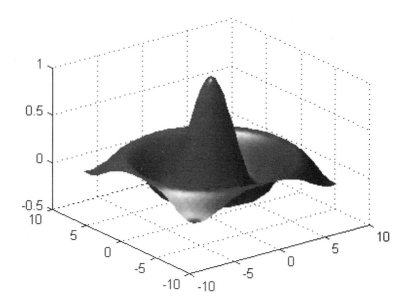

Manipulating the Surface

The figure toolbar and the camera toolbar provide ways to explore 3-D graphics interactively. Display the camera toolbar by selecting **Camera Toolbar** from the figure **View** menu.

The following picture shows both toolbars with the **Rotate 3D** tool selected.

These tools enable you to move the camera around the surface object, zoom, add lighting, and perform other viewing operations without issuing commands.

The following picture shows the surface viewed by orbiting the camera toward the bottom using **Rotate 3D**. A scene light has been added to illuminate the underside of the surface, which is not lit by the light added in the previous section.

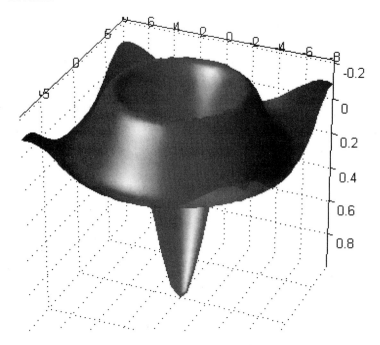

For More Information See "Lighting as a Visualization Tool" and "View Control with the Camera Toolbar" in the MATLAB 3-D Visualization documentation for details about these techniques.

Plotting Image Data

Two-dimensional arrays can be displayed as *images*, where the array elements determine brightness or color of the images. For example, the statements

```
load durer
whos
Name          Size         Bytes  Class

   X          648x509    2638656  double array
   caption    2x28           112  char array
   map        128x3         3072  double array
```

load the file durer.mat, adding three variables to the workspace. The matrix X is a 648-by-509 matrix and map is a 128-by-3 matrix that is the colormap for this image.

MAT-files, such as durer.mat, are binary files that can be created on one platform and later read by MATLAB on a different platform.

The elements of X are integers between 1 and 128, which serve as indices into the colormap, map. Then

```
image(X)
colormap(map)
axis image
```

reproduces Albrecht Dürer's etching shown in "Matrices and Magic Squares" on page 2-2. A high-resolution scan of the magic square in the upper-right corner is available in another file. Type

```
load detail
```

and then use the up arrow key on your keyboard to reexecute the image, colormap, and axis commands. The statement

```
colormap(hot)
```

adds some 21st century colorization to the sixteenth century etching. The function hot generates a colormap containing shades of reds, oranges, and yellows. Typically a given image matrix has a specific colormap associated with it. See the colormap reference page for a list of other predefined colormaps.

Reading and Writing Images

You can read standard image files (TIFF, JPEG, BMP, etc.) into MATLAB using the imread function. The type of data returned by imread depends on the type of image you are reading.

You can write MATLAB data to a variety of standard image formats using the imwrite function. See the MATLAB reference pages for these functions for more information and examples.

For More Information See "Displaying Bit-Mapped Images" in the MATLAB Graphics documentation for details about the image processing capabilities of MATLAB.

Printing Graphics

- "Printing from the Menu" on page 3-71
- "Exporting the Figure to a Graphics File" on page 3-71
- "Using the Print Command" on page 3-72

You can print a MATLAB figure directly on a printer connected to your computer or you can export the figure to one of the standard graphics file formats supported by MATLAB. There are two ways to print and export figures:

- Use the **Print** or **Export Setup** options under the **File** menu.
- Use the `print` command to print or export the figure.

See "Preparing Graphs for Presentation" on page 3-37 for an example.

Printing from the Menu

There are two menu options under the **File** menu that pertain to printing:

- The **Print Preview** option displays a dialog box that lets you lay out and style figures for printing while previewing the output page, and from which you can print the figure. It includes options that formerly were part of the Page Setup dialog box.
- The **Print** option displays a dialog box that lets you choose a printer, select standard printing options, and print the figure.

Use **Print Preview** to determine whether the printed output is what you want. Click the Print Preview dialog box **Help** button to display information on how to set up the page.

For details on printing from GUIs and from the Command Window, see "Printing and Exporting" in the MATLAB Graphics documentation.

Exporting the Figure to a Graphics File

The **Export Setup** option in the **File** menu enables you to set a variety of figure characteristics, such as size and font type, as well as apply predefined templates to achieve standard-looking graphics files. After setup, you can export the figure to a number of standard graphics file formats.

Using the Print Command

The `print` command provides more flexibility in the type of output sent to the printer and allows you to control printing from M-files. The result can be sent directly to your default printer or stored in a specified file. A wide variety of output formats, including TIFF, JPEG, and PostScript, is available.

For example, this statement saves the contents of the current figure window as color Encapsulated Level 2 PostScript in the file called `magicsquare.eps`. It also includes a TIFF preview, which enables most word processors to display the picture.

```
print -depsc2 -tiff magicsquare.eps
```

To save the same figure as a TIFF file with a resolution of 200 dpi, use the following command:

```
print -dtiff -r200 magicsquare.tiff
```

If you type `print` on the command line,

```
print
```

MATLAB prints the current figure on your default printer.

For More Information See the `print` reference page and "Printing and Exporting" in the MATLAB Graphics documentation for details about printing.

Handle Graphics

Handle Graphics refers to a system of graphics objects that MATLAB uses to implement graphing and visualization functions. Each object created has a fixed set of properties. You can use these properties to control the behavior and appearance of your graph.

When you call a plotting function, MATLAB creates the graph using various graphics objects, such as a figure window, axes, lines, text, and so on. MATLAB enables you to query the value of each property and set the values of most properties.

For example, the following statement creates a figure with a white background color and without displaying the figure toolbar:

```
figure('Color','white','Toolbar','none')
```

Using the Handle

Whenever MATLAB creates a graphics object, it assigns an identifier (called a *handle*) to the object. You can use this handle to access the object's properties with the set and get functions. For example, the following statements create a graph and return a handle to a lineseries object in h:

```
x = 1:10;
y = x.^3;
h = plot(x,y);
```

You can use the handle h to set the properties of the lineseries object. For example, you can set its Color property:

```
set(h,'Color','red')
```

You can also specify properties when you call the plotting function:

```
h = plot(x,y,'Color','red');
```

When you query the lineseries properties,

```
get(h,'LineWidth')
```

MATLAB returns the answer:

```
ans =
 0.5000
```

Use the handle to see what properties a particular object contains:

```
get(h)
```

Graphics Objects

Graphics objects are the basic elements used to display graphs and user interface components. These objects are organized into a hierarchy, as shown by the following diagram.

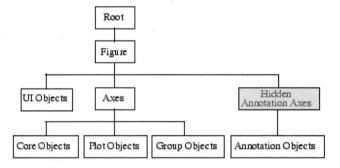

Key Graphics Objects

When you call a function to create a graph, MATLAB creates a hierarchy of graphics objects. For example, calling the plot function creates the following graphics objects:

- Lineseries plot objects — Represent the data passed to the plot function.

- Axes — Provide a frame of reference and scaling for the plotted lineseries.

- Text — Label the axes tick marks and are used for titles and annotations.
- Figures — Are the windows that contain axes toolbars, menus, etc.

Different types of graphs use different objects to represent data; however, all data objects are contained in axes and all objects (except root) are contained in figures.

The root is an abstract object that primarily stores information about your computer or MATLAB state. You cannot create an instance of the root object.

For More Information See "Handle Graphics Objects" in the MATLAB Graphics documentation for details about graphics objects.

User interface objects are used to create graphical user interfaces (GUIs). These objects include components like push buttons, editable text boxes, and list boxes.

For More Information See Chapter 6, "Creating Graphical User Interfaces" for details about user interface objects.

Creating Objects
Plotting functions (like plot and surf) call the appropriate low-level function to draw their respective graph. For information about an object's properties, you can use the Handle Graphics Property Browser in the MATLAB online Graphics documentation.

Functions for Working with Objects
This table lists functions commonly used when working with objects.

Function	Purpose
allchild	Find all children of specified objects.
ancestor	Find ancestor of graphics object.

Function	Purpose
copyobj	Copy graphics object.
delete	Delete an object.
findall	Find all graphics objects (including hidden handles).
findobj	Find the handles of objects having specified property values.
gca	Return the handle of the current axes.
gcf	Return the handle of the current figure.
gco	Return the handle of the current object.
get	Query the values of an object's properties.
ishandle	True if the value is a valid object handle.
set	Set the values of an object's properties.

Setting Object Properties

All object properties have default values. However, you might find it useful to change the settings of some properties to customize your graph. There are two ways to set object properties:

- Specify values for properties when you create the object.

- Set the property value on an object that already exists.

Setting Properties from Plotting Commands

You can specify object property value pairs as arguments to many plotting functions, such as plot, mesh, and surf.

For example, plotting commands that create lineseries or surfaceplot objects enable you to specify property name/property value pairs as arguments. The command

```
surf(x,y,z,'FaceColor','interp',...
    'FaceLighting','gouraud')
```

plots the data in the variables x, y, and z using a surfaceplot object with interpolated face color and employing the Gouraud face light technique. You can set any of the object's properties this way.

Setting Properties of Existing Objects

To modify the property values of existing objects, you can use the set command or the Property Editor. This section describes how to use the set command. See "Using the Property Editor" on page 3-18 for more information.

Most plotting functions return the handles of the objects that they create so you can modify the objects using the set command. For example, these statements plot a 5-by-5 matrix (creating five lineseries, one per column), and then set the Marker property to a square and the MarkerFaceColor property to green:

```
h = plot(magic(5));
set(h,'Marker','s','MarkerFaceColor','g')
```

In this case, h is a vector containing five handles, one for each of the five lineseries in the graph. The set statement sets the Marker and MarkerFaceColor properties of all lineseries to the same values.

Setting Multiple Property Values

If you want to set the properties of each lineseries to a different value, you can use cell arrays to store all the data and pass it to the set command. For example, create a plot and save the lineseries handles:

```
h = plot(magic(5));
```

Suppose you want to add different markers to each lineseries and color the marker's face color the same color as the lineseries. You need to define two cell arrays—one containing the property names and the other containing the desired values of the properties.

The prop_name cell array contains two elements:

```
prop_name(1) = {'Marker'};
prop_name(2) = {'MarkerFaceColor'};
```

The prop_values cell array contains 10 values: five values for the Marker property and five values for the MarkerFaceColor property. Notice that prop_values is a two-dimensional cell array. The first dimension indicates which handle in h the values apply to and the second dimension indicates which property the value is assigned to:

```
prop_values(1,1) = {'s'};
prop_values(1,2) = {get(h(1),'Color')};
prop_values(2,1) = {'d'};
prop_values(2,2) = {get(h(2),'Color')};
prop_values(3,1) = {'o'};
prop_values(3,2) = {get(h(3),'Color')};
prop_values(4,1) = {'p'};
prop_values(4,2) = {get(h(4),'Color')};
prop_values(5,1) = {'h'};
prop_values(5,2) = {get(h(5),'Color')};
```

The MarkerFaceColor is always assigned the value of the corresponding line's color (obtained by getting the lineseries Color property with the get command).

After defining the cell arrays, call set to specify the new property values:

```
set(h,prop_name,prop_values)
```

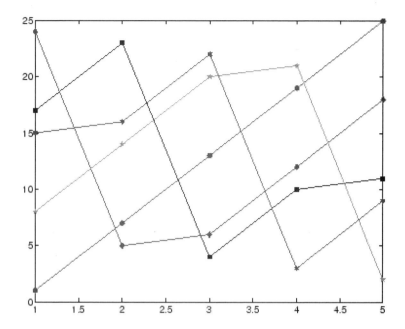

Specifying the Axes or Figure

MATLAB always creates an axes or figure if one does not exist when you issue a plotting command. However, when you are creating a graphics M-file, it is good practice to explicitly create and specify the parent axes and figure, particularly if others will use your program. Specifying the parent prevents the following problems:

- Your M-file overwrites the graph in the current figure. Note that a figure becomes the current figure whenever a user clicks it.

- The current figure might be in an unexpected state and not behave as your program expects.

The following example shows a simple M-file that plots a function and the mean of the function over the specified range:

```
function myfunc(x)
% x = -10:.005:40; Here's a value you can use for x
y = [1.5*cos(x) + 6*exp(-.1*x) + exp(.07*x).*sin(3*x)];
ym = mean(y);
```

```
hfig = figure('Name','Function and Mean',...
   'Pointer','fullcrosshair');
hax = axes('Parent',hfig);
plot(hax,x,y)
hold on
plot(hax,[min(x) max(x)],[ym ym],'Color','red')
hold off
ylab = get(hax,'YTick');
set(hax,'YTick',sort([ylab ym]))
title ('y = 1.5cos(x) + 6e^{-0.1x} + e^{0.07x}sin(3x)')
xlabel('X Axis'); ylabel('Y Axis')
```

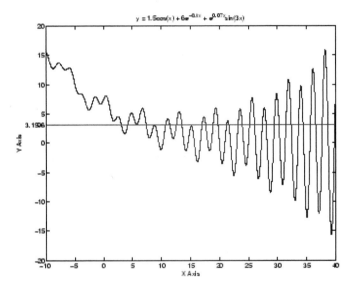

Finding the Handles of Existing Objects

The findobj function enables you to obtain the handles of graphics objects by searching for objects with particular property values. With findobj you can specify the values of any combination of properties, which makes it easy to pick one object out of many. findobj also recognizes regular expressions (regexp).

For example, you might want to find the blue line with square marker having blue face color. You can also specify which figures or axes to search, if there are more than one. The following four sections provide examples illustrating how to use findobj.

Finding All Objects of a Certain Type

Because all objects have a Type property that identifies the type of object, you can find the handles of all occurrences of a particular type of object. For example,

```
h = findobj('Type','patch');
```

finds the handles of all patch objects.

Finding Objects with a Particular Property

You can specify multiple properties to narrow the search. For example,

```
h = findobj('Type','line','Color','r','LineStyle',':');
```

finds the handles of all red dotted lines.

Limiting the Scope of the Search

You can specify the starting point in the object hierarchy by passing the handle of the starting figure or axes as the first argument. For example,

```
h = findobj(gca,'Type','text','String','\pi/2');
```

finds the string $\pi/2$ only within the current axes.

Using findobj as an Argument

Because findobj returns the handles it finds, you can use it in place of the handle argument. For example,

```
set(findobj('Type','line','Color','red'),'LineStyle',':')
```

finds all red lines and sets their line style to dotted.

Creating Animations

MATLAB provides three ways of generating moving, animated graphics:

- "Erase Mode Method" on page 3-82 — Continually erase and then redraw the objects on the screen, making incremental changes with each redraw.

- "Creating Movies" on page 3-83 — Save a number of different pictures and then play them back as a movie.

- Using AVI files. See avifile for more information and examples.

Erase Mode Method

Using the EraseMode property is appropriate for long sequences of simple plots where the change from frame to frame is minimal. Here is an example showing simulated Brownian motion. Specify a number of points, such as

```
n = 20
```

and a temperature or velocity, such as

```
s = .02
```

The best values for these two parameters depend upon the speed of your particular computer. Generate n random points with (x,y) coordinates between $-\frac{1}{2}$ and $+\frac{1}{2}$:

```
x = rand(n,1)-0.5;
y = rand(n,1)-0.5;
```

Plot the points in a square with sides at -1 and +1. Save the handle for the vector of points and set its EraseMode to xor. This tells the MATLAB graphics system not to redraw the entire plot when the coordinates of one point are changed, but to restore the background color in the vicinity of the point using an exclusive or operation:

```
h = plot(x,y,'.');
axis([-1 1 -1 1])
axis square
grid off
set(h,'EraseMode','xor','MarkerSize',18)
```

Now begin the animation. Here is an infinite while loop, which you can eventually exit by pressing **Ctrl+C**. Each time through the loop, add a small amount of normally distributed random noise to the coordinates of the points. Then, instead of creating an entirely new plot, simply change the XData and YData properties of the original plot:

```
while 1
    drawnow
    x = x + s*randn(n,1);
    y = y + s*randn(n,1);
    set(h,'XData',x,'YData',y)
end
```

See how long it takes for one of the points to get outside the square and how long before all the points are outside the square.

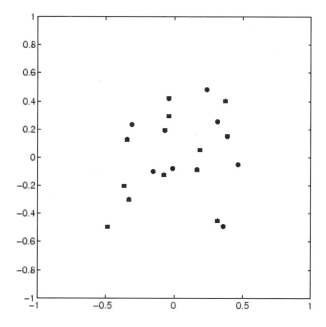

Creating Movies

If you increase the number of points in the Brownian motion example to n = 300 and s = .02, the motion is no longer very fluid; it takes too much time to draw each time step. It becomes more effective to save a predetermined number of frames as bitmaps and to play them back as a *movie*.

First, decide on the number of frames:

```
nframes = 50;
```

Next, set up the first plot as before, except using the default EraseMode (normal):

```
x = rand(n,1)-0.5;
y = rand(n,1)-0.5;
h = plot(x,y,'.');
set(h,'MarkerSize',18);
axis([-1 1 -1 1])
axis square
grid off
```

Generate the movie and use getframe to capture each frame:

```
for k = 1:nframes
    x = x + s*randn(n,1);
    y = y + s*randn(n,1);
    set(h,'XData',x,'YData',y)
    M(k) = getframe;
end
```

Finally, play the movie five times:

```
movie(M,5)
```

4

Programming

Flow Control (p. 4-2)

Use flow control constructs including if, `switch` and `case`, `for`, `while`, `continue`, and `break`.

Other Data Structures (p. 4-8)

Work with multidimensional arrays, cell arrays, character and text data, and structures.

Scripts and Functions (p. 4-19)

Write scripts and functions, use global variables, pass string arguments to functions, use `eval` to evaluate text expressions, vectorize code, preallocate arrays, reference functions using handles, and use functions that operate on functions.

Flow Control

MATLAB has several flow control constructs:

- "if, else, and elseif" on page 4-2
- "switch and case" on page 4-4
- "for" on page 4-5
- "while" on page 4-5
- "continue" on page 4-6
- "break" on page 4-6
- "try - catch" on page 4-7
- "return" on page 4-7

if, else, and elseif

The if statement evaluates a logical expression and executes a group of statements when the expression is *true*. The optional elseif and else keywords provide for the execution of alternate groups of statements. An end keyword, which matches the if, terminates the last group of statements. The groups of statements are delineated by the four keywords—no braces or brackets are involved.

The MATLAB algorithm for generating a magic square of order n involves three different cases: when n is odd, when n is even but not divisible by 4, or when n is divisible by 4. This is described by

```
if rem(n,2) ~= 0
   M = odd_magic(n)
elseif rem(n,4) ~= 0
   M = single_even_magic(n)
else
   M = double_even_magic(n)
end
```

For most values of n in this example, the three cases are mutually exclusive. For values that are not mutually exclusive, such as n=5, the first *true* condition is executed.

It is important to understand how relational operators and if statements work with matrices. When you want to check for equality between two variables, you might use

```
if A == B, ...
```

This is valid MATLAB code, and does what you expect when A and B are scalars. But when A and B are matrices, A == B does not test *if* they are equal, it tests *where* they are equal; the result is another matrix of 0's and 1's showing element-by-element equality. (In fact, if A and B are not the same size, then A == B is an error.)

```
A = magic(4);      B = A;     B(1,1) = 0;

A == B
ans =
      0    1    1    1
      1    1    1    1
      1    1    1    1
      1    1    1    1
```

The proper way to check for equality between two variables is to use the isequal function,

```
if isequal(A, B), ...
```

isequal returns a *scalar* logical value of 1 (representing true) or 0 (false), instead of a matrix, as the expression to be evaluated by the if function. Using the A and B matrices from above, you get

```
isequal(A, B)
ans =
      0
```

Here is another example to emphasize this point. If A and B are scalars, the following program will never reach the "unexpected situation". But for most pairs of matrices, including our magic squares with interchanged columns, none of the matrix conditions A > B, A < B, or A == B is true for *all* elements and so the else clause is executed:

```
if A > B
    'greater'
```

```
elseif A < B
   'less'
elseif A == B
   'equal'
else
   error('Unexpected situation')
end
```

Several functions are helpful for reducing the results of matrix comparisons to scalar conditions for use with if, including

```
isequal
isempty
all
any
```

switch and case

The switch statement executes groups of statements based on the value of a variable or expression. The keywords case and otherwise delineate the groups. Only the first matching case is executed. There must always be an end to match the switch.

The logic of the magic squares algorithm can also be described by

```
switch (rem(n,4)==0) + (rem(n,2)==0)
   case 0
      M = odd_magic(n)
   case 1
      M = single_even_magic(n)
   case 2
      M = double_even_magic(n)
   otherwise
      error('This is impossible')
end
```

Note Unlike the C language switch statement, MATLAB switch does not fall through. If the first case statement is true, the other case statements do not execute. So, break statements are not required.

---

for

The for loop repeats a group of statements a fixed, predetermined number of times. A matching end delineates the statements:

```
for n = 3:32
    r(n) = rank(magic(n));
end
r
```

The semicolon terminating the inner statement suppresses repeated printing, and the r after the loop displays the final result.

It is a good idea to indent the loops for readability, especially when they are nested:

```
for i = 1:m
    for j = 1:n
        H(i,j) = 1/(i+j);
    end
end
```

while

The while loop repeats a group of statements an indefinite number of times under control of a logical condition. A matching end delineates the statements.

Here is a complete program, illustrating while, if, else, and end, that uses interval bisection to find a zero of a polynomial:

```
a = 0; fa = -Inf;
b = 3; fb = Inf;
while b-a > eps*b
    x = (a+b)/2;
    fx = x^3-2*x-5;
    if sign(fx) == sign(fa)
        a = x; fa = fx;
    else
        b = x; fb = fx;
    end
end
x
```

The result is a root of the polynomial $x^3 - 2x - 5$, namely

```
x =
    2.09455148154233
```

The cautions involving matrix comparisons that are discussed in the section on the if statement also apply to the while statement.

continue

The continue statement passes control to the next iteration of the for loop or while loop in which it appears, skipping any remaining statements in the body of the loop. In nested loops, continue passes control to the next iteration of the for loop or while loop enclosing it.

The example below shows a continue loop that counts the lines of code in the file magic.m, skipping all blank lines and comments. A continue statement is used to advance to the next line in magic.m without incrementing the count whenever a blank line or comment line is encountered:

```
fid = fopen('magic.m','r');
count = 0;
while ~feof(fid)
    line = fgetl(fid);
    if isempty(line) | strncmp(line,'%',1)
        continue
    end
    count = count + 1;
end
disp(sprintf('%d lines',count));
```

break

The break statement lets you exit early from a for loop or while loop. In nested loops, break exits from the innermost loop only.

Here is an improvement on the example from the previous section. Why is this use of break a good idea?

```
a = 0; fa = -Inf;
b = 3; fb = Inf;
```

```
while b-a > eps*b
   x = (a+b)/2;
   fx = x^3-2*x-5;
   if fx == 0
      break
   elseif sign(fx) == sign(fa)
      a = x; fa = fx;
   else
      b = x; fb = fx;
   end
end
x
```

try - catch

The general form of a try-catch statement sequence is

```
try
   statement
   ...
   statement
catch
   statement
   ...
   statement
end
```

In this sequence the statements between try and catch are executed until an error occurs. The statements between catch and end are then executed. Use lasterr to see the cause of the error. If an error occurs between catch and end, MATLAB terminates execution unless another try-catch sequence has been established.

return

return terminates the current sequence of commands and returns control to the invoking function or to the keyboard. return is also used to terminate keyboard mode. A called function normally transfers control to the function that invoked it when it reaches the end of the function. You can insert a return statement within the called function to force an early termination and to transfer control to the invoking function.

Other Data Structures

This section introduces you to some other data structures in MATLAB, including

- "Multidimensional Arrays" on page 4-8
- "Cell Arrays" on page 4-10
- "Characters and Text" on page 4-12
- "Structures" on page 4-15

Multidimensional Arrays

Multidimensional arrays in MATLAB are arrays with more than two subscripts. One way of creating a multidimensional array is by calling zeros, ones, rand, or randn with more than two arguments. For example,

```
R = randn(3,4,5);
```

creates a 3-by-4-by-5 array with a total of 3*4*5 = 60 normally distributed random elements.

A three-dimensional array might represent three-dimensional physical data, say the temperature in a room, sampled on a rectangular grid. Or it might represent a sequence of matrices, $A^{(k)}$, or samples of a time-dependent matrix, $A(t)$. In these latter cases, the (i, j)th element of the kth matrix, or the t_kth matrix, is denoted by A(i,j,k).

MATLAB and Dürer's versions of the magic square of order 4 differ by an interchange of two columns. Many different magic squares can be generated by interchanging columns. The statement

```
p = perms(1:4);
```

generates the 4! = 24 permutations of 1:4. The kth permutation is the row vector p(k,:). Then

```
A = magic(4);
M = zeros(4,4,24);

for k = 1:24
```

```
    M(:,:,k) = A(:,p(k,:));
end
```

stores the sequence of 24 magic squares in a three-dimensional array, M. The size of M is

```
size(M)

ans =
    4    4   24
```

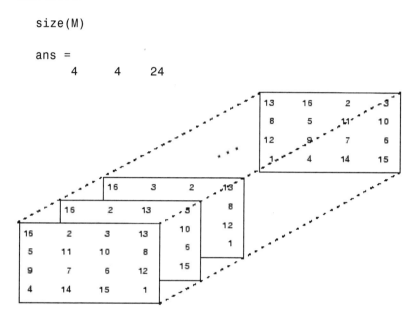

Note The order of the matrices shown in this illustration might differ from your results. The perms function always returns all permutations of the input vector, but the order of the permutations might be different for different MATLAB versions.

The statement

```
sum(M,d)
```

computes sums by varying the dth subscript. So

```
sum(M,1)
```

is a 1-by-4-by-24 array containing 24 copies of the row vector

4-9

```
34      34      34      34
```

and

```
sum(M,2)
```

is a 4-by-1-by-24 array containing 24 copies of the column vector

```
34
34
34
34
```

Finally,

```
S = sum(M,3)
```

adds the 24 matrices in the sequence. The result has size 4-by-4-by-1, so it looks like a 4-by-4 array:

```
S =
    204    204    204    204
    204    204    204    204
    204    204    204    204
    204    204    204    204
```

Cell Arrays

Cell arrays in MATLAB are multidimensional arrays whose elements are copies of other arrays. A cell array of empty matrices can be created with the cell function. But, more often, cell arrays are created by enclosing a miscellaneous collection of things in curly braces, {}. The curly braces are also used with subscripts to access the contents of various cells. For example,

```
C = {A sum(A) prod(prod(A))}
```

produces a 1-by-3 cell array. The three cells contain the magic square, the row vector of column sums, and the product of all its elements. When C is displayed, you see

```
C =
    [4x4 double]    [1x4 double]    [20922789888000]
```

This is because the first two cells are too large to print in this limited space, but the third cell contains only a single number, 16!, so there is room to print it.

Here are two important points to remember. First, to retrieve the contents of one of the cells, use subscripts in curly braces. For example, C{1} retrieves the magic square and C{3} is 16!. Second, cell arrays contain *copies* of other arrays, not *pointers* to those arrays. If you subsequently change A, nothing happens to C.

You can use three-dimensional arrays to store a sequence of matrices of the *same* size. Cell arrays can be used to store a sequence of matrices of *different* sizes. For example,

```
M = cell(8,1);
for n = 1:8
    M{n} = magic(n);
end
M
```

produces a sequence of magic squares of different order:

```
M =
    [                1]
    [ 2x2    double]
    [ 3x3    double]
    [ 4x4    double]
    [ 5x5    double]
    [ 6x6    double]
    [ 7x7    double]
    [ 8x8    double]
```

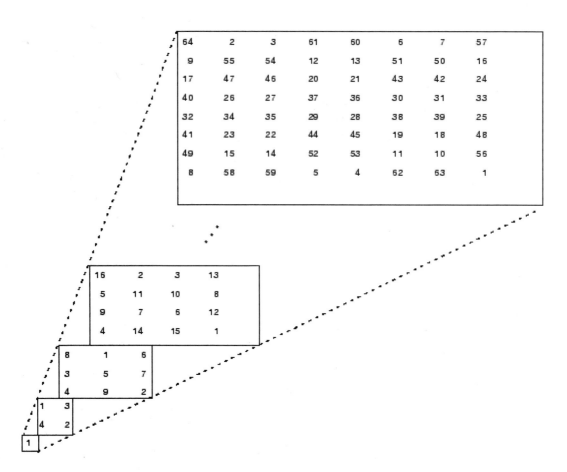

You can retrieve the 4-by-4 magic square matrix with

```
M{4}
```

Characters and Text

Enter text into MATLAB using single quotes. For example,

```
s = 'Hello'
```

The result is not the same kind of numeric matrix or array you have been dealing with up to now. It is a 1-by-5 character array.

Internally, the characters are stored as numbers, but not in floating-point format. The statement

```
a = double(s)
```

converts the character array to a numeric matrix containing floating-point representations of the ASCII codes for each character. The result is

```
a =
    72    101    108    108    111
```

The statement

```
s = char(a)
```

reverses the conversion.

Converting numbers to characters makes it possible to investigate the various fonts available on your computer. The printable characters in the basic ASCII character set are represented by the integers 32:127. (The integers less than 32 represent nonprintable control characters.) These integers are arranged in an appropriate 6-by-16 array with

```
F = reshape(32:127,16,6)';
```

The printable characters in the extended ASCII character set are represented by F+128. When these integers are interpreted as characters, the result depends on the font currently being used. Type the statements

```
char(F)
char(F+128)
```

and then vary the font being used for the Command Window. Select **Preferences** from the **File** menu to change the font. If you include tabs in lines of code, use a fixed-width font, such as Monospaced, to align the tab positions on different lines.

Concatenation with square brackets joins text variables together into larger strings. The statement

```
h = [s, ' world']
```

joins the strings horizontally and produces

```
h =
    Hello world
```

The statement

```
v = [s; 'world']
```

joins the strings vertically and produces

```
v =
    Hello
    world
```

Note that a blank has to be inserted before the `'w'` in h and that both words in v have to have the same length. The resulting arrays are both character arrays; h is 1-by-11 and v is 2-by-5.

To manipulate a body of text containing lines of different lengths, you have two choices—a padded character array or a cell array of strings. When creating a character array, you must make each row of the array the same length. (Pad the ends of the shorter rows with spaces.) The char function does this padding for you. For example,

```
S = char('A','rolling','stone','gathers','momentum.')
```

produces a 5-by-9 character array:

```
S =
A
rolling
stone
gathers
momentum.
```

Alternatively, you can store the text in a cell array. For example,

```
C = {'A';'rolling';'stone';'gathers';'momentum.'}
```

creates a 5-by-1 cell array that requires no padding because each row of the array can have a different length:

```
C =
    'A'
    'rolling'
    'stone'
    'gathers'
    'momentum.'
```

You can convert a padded character array to a cell array of strings with

```
C = cellstr(S)
```

and reverse the process with

```
S = char(C)
```

Structures

Structures are multidimensional MATLAB arrays with elements accessed by textual *field designators*. For example,

```
S.name = 'Ed Plum';
S.score = 83;
S.grade = 'B+'
```

creates a scalar structure with three fields:

```
S =
     name: 'Ed Plum'
    score: 83
    grade: 'B+'
```

Like everything else in MATLAB, structures are arrays, so you can insert additional elements. In this case, each element of the array is a structure with several fields. The fields can be added one at a time,

```
S(2).name = 'Toni Miller';
S(2).score = 91;
S(2).grade = 'A-';
```

or an entire element can be added with a single statement:

```
S(3) = struct('name','Jerry Garcia',...
              'score',70,'grade','C')
```

Now the structure is large enough that only a summary is printed:

```
S =
1x3 struct array with fields:
    name
    score
    grade
```

There are several ways to reassemble the various fields into other MATLAB arrays. They are mostly based on the notation of a *comma-separated list*. If you type

```
S.score
```

it is the same as typing

```
S(1).score, S(2).score, S(3).score
```

which is a comma-separated list.

If you enclose the expression that generates such a list within square brackets, MATLAB stores each item from the list in an array. In this example, MATLAB creates a numeric row vector containing the score field of each element of structure array S:

```
scores = [S.score]
scores =
    83    91    70

avg_score = sum(scores)/length(scores)
avg_score =
    81.3333
```

To create a character array from one of the text fields (name, for example), call the char function on the comma-separated list produced by S.name:

```
names = char(S.name)
names =
    Ed Plum
    Toni Miller
    Jerry Garcia
```

Similarly, you can create a cell array from the name fields by enclosing the list-generating expression within curly braces:

```
names = {S.name}
names =
    'Ed Plum'    'Toni Miller'    'Jerry Garcia'
```

To assign the fields of each element of a structure array to separate variables outside of the structure, specify each output to the left of the equals sign, enclosing them all within square brackets:

```
[N1 N2 N3] = S.name
N1 =
    Ed Plum
N2 =
    Toni Miller
N3 =
    Jerry Garcia
```

Dynamic Field Names

The most common way to access the data in a structure is by specifying the name of the field that you want to reference. Another means of accessing structure data is to use dynamic field names. These names express the field as a variable expression that MATLAB evaluates at run-time. The dot-parentheses syntax shown here makes expression a dynamic field name:

```
structName.(expression)
```

Index into this field using the standard MATLAB indexing syntax. For example, to evaluate expression into a field name and obtain the values of that field at columns 1 through 25 of row 7, use

```
structName.(expression)(7,1:25)
```

Dynamic Field Names Example. The avgscore function shown below computes an average test score, retrieving information from the testscores structure using dynamic field names:

```
function avg = avgscore(testscores, student, first, last)
for k = first:last
    scores(k) = testscores.(student).week(k);
```

```
end
avg = sum(scores)/(last - first + 1);
```

You can run this function using different values for the dynamic field student. First, initialize the structure that contains scores for a 25 week period:

```
testscores.Ann_Lane.week(1:25) = ...
  [95 89 76 82 79 92 94 92 89 81 75 93 ...
   85 84 83 86 85 90 82 82 84 79 96 88 98];

testscores.William_King.week(1:25) = ...
  [87 80 91 84 99 87 93 87 97 87 82 89 ...
   86 82 90 98 75 79 92 84 90 93 84 78 81];
```

Now run avgscore, supplying the students name fields for the testscores structure at runtime using dynamic field names:

```
avgscore(testscores, 'Ann_Lane', 7, 22)
ans =
   85.2500

avgscore(testscores, 'William_King', 7, 22)
ans =
   87.7500
```

Scripts and Functions

Topics covered in this section are

MATLAB is a powerful programming language as well as an interactive computational environment. Files that contain code in the MATLAB language are called M-files. You create M-files using a text editor, then use them as you would any other MATLAB function or command.

There are two kinds of M-files:

- Scripts, which do not accept input arguments or return output arguments. They operate on data in the workspace.
- Functions, which can accept input arguments and return output arguments. Internal variables are local to the function.

If you're a new MATLAB programmer, just create the M-files that you want to try out in the current directory. As you develop more of your own M-files, you will want to organize them into other directories and personal toolboxes that you can add to your MATLAB search path.

If you duplicate function names, MATLAB executes the one that occurs first in the search path.

To view the contents of an M-file, for example, `myfunction.m`, use

```
type myfunction
```

Scripts

When you invoke a *script*, MATLAB simply executes the commands found in the file. Scripts can operate on existing data in the workspace, or they can create new data on which to operate. Although scripts do not return output arguments, any variables that they create remain in the workspace, to be used in subsequent computations. In addition, scripts can produce graphical output using functions like `plot`.

For example, create a file called `magicrank.m` that contains these MATLAB commands:

```
% Investigate the rank of magic squares
r = zeros(1,32);
for n = 3:32
    r(n) = rank(magic(n));
end
r
bar(r)
```

Typing the statement

```
magicrank
```

causes MATLAB to execute the commands, compute the rank of the first 30 magic squares, and plot a bar graph of the result. After execution of the file is complete, the variables n and r remain in the workspace.

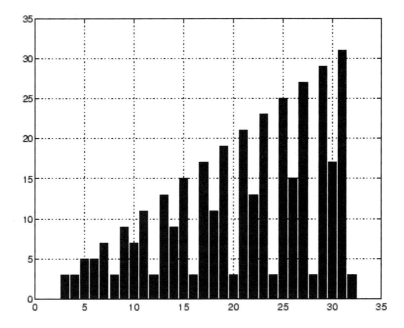

Functions

Functions are M-files that can accept input arguments and return output arguments. The names of the M-file and of the function should be the same. Functions operate on variables within their own workspace, separate from the workspace you access at the MATLAB command prompt.

A good example is provided by rank. The M-file rank.m is available in the directory

```
toolbox/matlab/matfun
```

You can see the file with

```
type rank
```

Here is the file:

```
function r = rank(A,tol)
%    RANK Matrix rank.
%    RANK(A) provides an estimate of the number of linearly
```

```
%     independent rows or columns of a matrix A.
%     RANK(A,tol) is the number of singular values of A
%     that are larger than tol.
%     RANK(A) uses the default tol = max(size(A)) * norm(A) * eps.

s = svd(A);
if nargin==1
   tol = max(size(A)') * max(s) * eps;
end
r = sum(s > tol);
```

The first line of a function M-file starts with the keyword function. It gives the function name and order of arguments. In this case, there are up to two input arguments and one output argument.

The next several lines, up to the first blank or executable line, are comment lines that provide the help text. These lines are printed when you type

```
help rank
```

The first line of the help text is the H1 line, which MATLAB displays when you use the lookfor command or request help on a directory.

The rest of the file is the executable MATLAB code defining the function. The variable s introduced in the body of the function, as well as the variables on the first line, r, A and tol, are all *local* to the function; they are separate from any variables in the MATLAB workspace.

This example illustrates one aspect of MATLAB functions that is not ordinarily found in other programming languages—a variable number of arguments. The rank function can be used in several different ways:

```
rank(A)
r = rank(A)
r = rank(A,1.e-6)
```

Many M-files work this way. If no output argument is supplied, the result is stored in ans. If the second input argument is not supplied, the function computes a default value. Within the body of the function, two quantities named nargin and nargout are available which tell you the number of input and output arguments involved in each particular use of the function. The rank function uses nargin, but does not need to use nargout.

Types of Functions

MATLAB offers several different types of functions to use in your programming.

Anonymous Functions

An *anonymous function* is a simple form of MATLAB function that does not require an M-file. It consists of a single MATLAB expression and any number of input and output arguments. You can define an anonymous function right at the MATLAB command line, or within an M-file function or script. This gives you a quick means of creating simple functions without having to create M-files each time.

The syntax for creating an anonymous function from an expression is

```
f = @(arglist)expression
```

The statement below creates an anonymous function that finds the square of a number. When you call this function, MATLAB assigns the value you pass in to variable x, and then uses x in the equation x.^2:

```
sqr = @(x) x.^2;
```

To execute the sqr function defined above, type

```
a = sqr(5)
a =
    25
```

Primary and Subfunctions

All functions that are not anonymous must be defined within an M-file. Each M-file has a required *primary function* that appears first in the file, and any number of *subfunctions* that follow the primary. Primary functions have a wider scope than subfunctions. That is, primary functions can be invoked from outside of their M-file (from the MATLAB command line or from functions in other M-files) while subfunctions cannot. Subfunctions are visible only to the primary function and other subfunctions within their own M-file.

The rank function shown in the section on "Functions" on page 4-21 is an example of a primary function.

Private Functions

A *private function* is a type of primary M-file function. Its unique characteristic is that it is visible only to a limited group of other functions. This type of function can be useful if you want to limit access to a function, or when you choose not to expose the implementation of a function.

Private functions reside in subdirectories with the special name private. They are visible only to functions in the parent directory. For example, assume the directory newmath is on the MATLAB search path. A subdirectory of newmath called private can contain functions that only the functions in newmath can call.

Because private functions are invisible outside the parent directory, they can use the same names as functions in other directories. This is useful if you want to create your own version of a particular function while retaining the original in another directory. Because MATLAB looks for private functions before standard M-file functions, it will find a private function named test.m before a nonprivate M-file named test.m.

Nested Functions

You can define functions within the body of any MATLAB M-file function. These are said to be *nested* within the outer function. A nested function contains any or all of the components of any other M-file function. In this example, function B is nested in function A:

```
function x = A(p1, p2)
...
B(p2)
   function y = B(p3)
   ...
   end
...
end
```

Like other functions, a nested function has its own workspace where variables used by the function are stored. But it also has access to the workspaces of all functions in which it is nested. So, for example, a variable that has a value assigned to it by the primary function can be read or overwritten by a function nested at any level within the primary. Similarly, a variable that is assigned in a nested function can be read or overwritten by any of the functions containing that function.

Function Overloading

Overloaded functions act the same way as overloaded functions in most computer languages. Overloaded functions are useful when you need to create a function that responds to different types of inputs accordingly. For instance, you might want one of your functions to accept both double-precision and integer input, but to handle each type somewhat differently. You can make this difference invisible to the user by creating two separate functions having the same name, and designating one to handle double types and one to handle integers. When you call the function, MATLAB chooses which M-file to dispatch to based on the type of the input arguments.

Global Variables

If you want more than one function to share a single copy of a variable, simply declare the variable as global in all the functions. Do the same thing at the command line if you want the base workspace to access the variable. The global declaration must occur before the variable is actually used in a function. Although it is not required, using capital letters for the names of global variables helps distinguish them from other variables. For example, create an M-file called falling.m:

```
function h = falling(t)
global GRAVITY
h = 1/2*GRAVITY*t.^2;
```

Then interactively enter the statements

```
global GRAVITY
GRAVITY = 32;
y = falling((0:.1:5)');
```

The two global statements make the value assigned to GRAVITY at the command prompt available inside the function. You can then modify GRAVITY interactively and obtain new solutions without editing any files.

Passing String Arguments to Functions

You can write MATLAB functions that accept string arguments without the parentheses and quotes. That is, MATLAB interprets

```
foo a b c
```

as

```
foo('a','b','c')
```

However, when you use the unquoted form, MATLAB cannot return output arguments. For example,

```
legend apples oranges
```

creates a legend on a plot using the strings apples and oranges as labels. If you want the legend command to return its output arguments, then you must use the quoted form:

```
[legh,objh] = legend('apples','oranges');
```

In addition, you must use the quoted form if any of the arguments is not a string.

Caution While the unquoted syntax is convenient, in some cases it can be used incorrectly without causing MATLAB to generate an error.

Constructing String Arguments in Code

The quoted form enables you to construct string arguments within the code. The following example processes multiple data files, August1.dat, August2.dat, and so on. It uses the function int2str, which converts an integer to a character, to build the filename:

```
for d = 1:31
```

```
      s = ['August' int2str(d) '.dat'];
      load(s)
      % Code to process the contents of the d-th file
   end
```

The eval Function

The eval function works with text variables to implement a powerful text
macro facility. The expression or statement

```
   eval(s)
```

uses the MATLAB interpreter to evaluate the expression or execute the
statement contained in the text string s.

The example of the previous section could also be done with the following
code, although this would be somewhat less efficient because it involves the
full interpreter, not just a function call:

```
   for d = 1:31
      s = ['load August' int2str(d) '.dat'];
      eval(s)
      % Process the contents of the d-th file
   end
```

Function Handles

You can create a handle to any MATLAB function and then use that handle
as a means of referencing the function. A function handle is typically passed
in an argument list to other functions, which can then execute, or *evaluate*,
the function using the handle.

Construct a function handle in MATLAB using the *at* sign, @, before the
function name. The following example creates a function handle for the sin
function and assigns it to the variable fhandle:

```
   fhandle = @sin;
```

You can call a function by means of its handle in the same way that you would
call the function using its name. The syntax is

```
   fhandle(arg1, arg2, ...);
```

The function `plot_fhandle`, shown below, receives a function handle and data, generates y-axis data using the function handle, and plots it:

```
function x = plot_fhandle(fhandle, data)
plot(data, fhandle(data))
```

When you call `plot_fhandle` with a handle to the `sin` function and the argument shown below, the resulting evaluation produces a sine wave plot:

```
plot_fhandle(@sin, -pi:0.01:pi)
```

Function Functions

A class of functions called "function functions" works with nonlinear functions of a scalar variable. That is, one function works on another function. The function functions include

- Zero finding

- Optimization

- Quadrature

- Ordinary differential equations

MATLAB represents the nonlinear function by a function M-file. For example, here is a simplified version of the function `humps` from the `matlab/demos` directory:

```
function y = humps(x)
y = 1./((x-.3).^2 + .01) + 1./((x-.9).^2 + .04) - 6;
```

Evaluate this function at a set of points in the interval $0 \leq x \leq 1$ with

```
x = 0:.002:1;
y = humps(x);
```

Then plot the function with

```
plot(x,y)
```

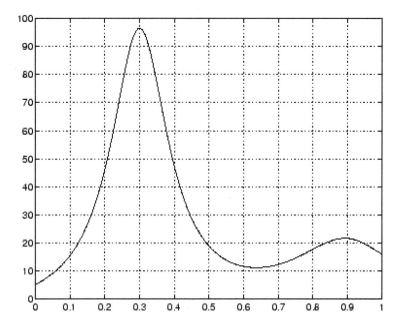

The graph shows that the function has a local minimum near $x = 0.6$. The function fminsearch finds the *minimizer*, the value of x where the function takes on this minimum. The first argument to fminsearch is a function handle to the function being minimized and the second argument is a rough guess at the location of the minimum:

```
p = fminsearch(@humps,.5)
p =
    0.6370
```

To evaluate the function at the minimizer,

```
humps(p)

ans =
    11.2528
```

Numerical analysts use the terms *quadrature* and *integration* to distinguish between numerical approximation of definite integrals and numerical integration of ordinary differential equations. MATLAB quadrature routines are quad and quadl. The statement

```
Q = quadl(@humps,0,1)
```

computes the area under the curve in the graph and produces

```
Q =
    29.8583
```

Finally, the graph shows that the function is never zero on this interval. So, if you search for a zero with

```
z = fzero(@humps,.5)
```

you will find one outside the interval

```
z =
    -0.1316
```

Vectorization

One way to make your MATLAB programs run faster is to vectorize the algorithms you use in constructing the programs. Where other programming languages might use `for` loops or `DO` loops, MATLAB can use vector or matrix operations. A simple example involves creating a table of logarithms:

```
x = .01;
for k = 1:1001
    y(k) = log10(x);
    x = x + .01;
end
```

A vectorized version of the same code is

```
x = .01:.01:10;
y = log10(x);
```

For more complicated code, vectorization options are not always so obvious.

For More Information See "Improving Performance and Memory Usage" in the MATLAB Programming documentation for other techniques that you can use.

Preallocation

If you cannot vectorize a piece of code, you can make your for loops go faster by preallocating any vectors or arrays in which output results are stored. For example, this code uses the function zeros to preallocate the vector created in the for loop. This makes the for loop execute significantly faster:

```
r = zeros(32,1);
for n = 1:32
    r(n) = rank(magic(n));
end
```

Without the preallocation in the previous example, the MATLAB interpreter enlarges the r vector by one element each time through the loop. Vector preallocation eliminates this step and results in faster execution.

5

Data Analysis

Introduction

Every data analysis has some standard components:

- Preprocessing — Consider outliers and missing values, and smooth data to identify possible models.
- Summarizing — Compute basic statistics to describe the overall location, scale, and shape of the data.
- Visualizing — Plot data to identify patterns and trends.
- Modeling — Give data trends fuller descriptions, suitable for predicting new values.

Data analysis moves among these components with two basic goals in mind:

1 Describe the patterns in the data with simple models that lead to accurate predictions.

2 Understand the relationships among variables that lead to the model.

This section of the Getting Started guide explains how to use MATLAB to carry out a basic data analysis.

Preprocessing Data

Note This section begins a data analysis that is continued in "Summarizing Data" on page 5-10, "Visualizing Data" on page 5-14, and "Modeling Data" on page 5-19.

Begin a data analysis by loading data into suitable MATLAB container variables and sorting out the "good" data from the "bad." This is a preliminary step that assures meaningful conclusions in subsequent parts of the analysis.

- "Loading the Data" on page 5-3
- "Missing Data" on page 5-3
- "Outliers" on page 5-4
- "Smoothing and Filtering" on page 5-6

Loading the Data

Begin by loading the data in `count.dat`:

```
load count.dat
```

The 24-by-3 array `count` contains hourly traffic counts (the rows) at three intersections (the columns) for a single day.

See "MATLAB for Data Analysis" and "Importing and Exporting Data" in the MATLAB Data Analysis documentation for more information on storing data in MATLAB variables for analysis.

Missing Data

In MATLAB, `NaN` (Not a Number) values represent missing data. `NaN` values allow variables with missing data to maintain their structure—in this case, 24-by-1 vectors with consistent indexing across all three intersections.

Check the data at the third intersection for `NaN` values using the MATLAB `isnan` function:

```
c3 = count(:,3); % Data at intersection 3
c3NaNCount = sum(isnan(c3))
c3NaNCount =
     0
```

isnan returns a logical vector the same size as c3, with entries indicating the presence (1) or absence (0) of NaN values for each of the 24 elements in the data. In this case, the logical values sum to 0, so there are no NaN values in the data.

NaN values are introduced into the data in the section on "Outliers" on page 5-4.

See "Removing and Interpolating Missing Values" in the MATLAB Data Analysis documentation for more information on handling missing data in MATLAB.

Outliers

Outliers are data values that are dramatically different from patterns in the rest of the data. They may be due to measurement error, or they may represent significant features in the data. Identifying outliers, and deciding what to do with them, depends on an understanding of the data and its source.

One common method for identifying outliers is to look for values more than a certain number of standard deviations σ from the mean μ. The following code plots a histogram of the data at the third intersection together with lines at μ and $\mu + n\sigma$, for $n = 1, 2$:

```
bin_counts = hist(c3); % Histogram bin counts
N = max(bin_counts); % Maximum bin count
mu3 = mean(c3); % Data mean
sigma3 = std(c3); % Data standard deviation

hist(c3) % Plot histogram
hold on
plot([mu3 mu3],[0 N],'r','LineWidth',2) % Mean
X = repmat(mu3+(1:2)*sigma3,2,1);
Y = repmat([0;N],1,2);
plot(X,Y,'g','LineWidth',2) % Standard deviations
```

```
legend('Data','Mean','Stds')
hold off
```

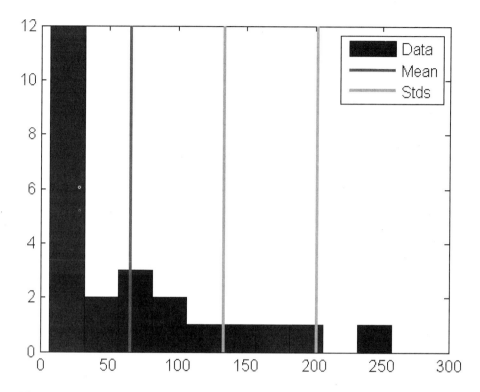

The plot shows that some of the data are more than two standard deviations above the mean. If you identify these data as errors (not features), replace them with NaN values as follows:

```
outliers = (c3 - mu3) > 2*sigma3;
c3m = c3; % Copy c3 to c3m
c3m(outliers) = NaN; % Add NaN values
```

See "Removing Outliers" in the MATLAB Data Analysis documentation for more information on handling outliers in MATLAB.

Smoothing and Filtering

A time-series plot of the data at the third intersection (with the outlier removed in "Outliers" on page 5-4) looks like this:

```
plot(c3m,'o-')
hold on
```

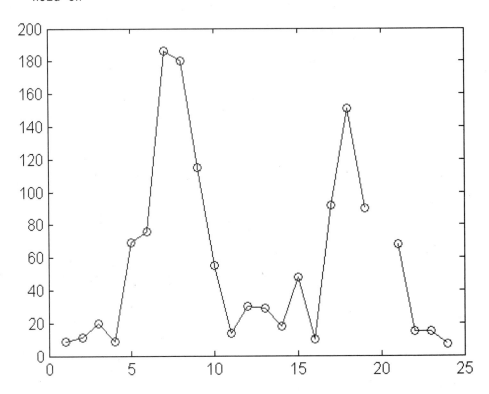

The NaN value at hour 20 appears as a gap in the plot. This handling of NaN values is typical of MATLAB plotting functions.

Noisy data shows random variations about expected values. You may want to smooth the data to reveal its main features before building a model. Two basic assumptions underlie smoothing:

- The relationship between the predictor (time) and the response (traffic volume) is smooth.

- The smoothing algorithm results in values that are better estimates of expected values because the noise has been reduced.

Apply a simple moving average smoother to the data using the MATLAB convn function:

```
span = 3; % Size of the averaging window
window = ones(span,1)/span;
smoothed_c3m = convn(c3m,window,'same');

h = plot(smoothed_c3m,'ro-');
legend('Data','Smoothed Data')
```

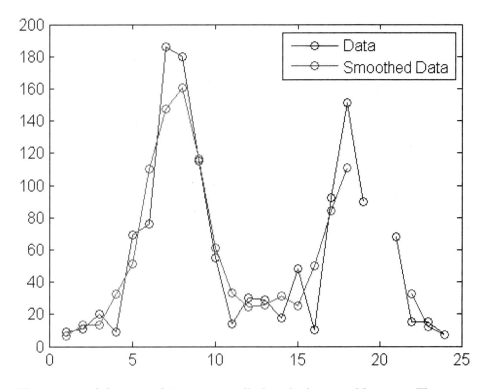

The extent of the smoothing is controlled with the variable span. The averaging calculation returns NaN values whenever the smoothing window includes the NaN value in the data, thus increasing the size of the gap in the smoothed data.

The MATLAB `filter` function is also used for smoothing data:

```
smoothed2_c3m = filter(window,1,c3m);

delete(h)
plot(smoothed2_c3m,'ro-');
```

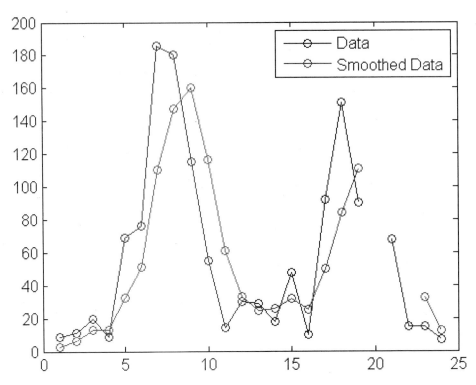

The smoothed data are shifted from the previous plot. `convn` with the `'same'` parameter returns the central part of the convolution, the same length as the data. `filter` returns the initial part of the convolution, the same length as the data. Otherwise, the algorithms are identical.

Smoothing estimates the center of the distribution of response values at each value of the predictor. It invalidates a basic assumption of many fitting algorithms, namely, that the errors at each value of the predictor are normally distributed. Accordingly, smoothed data should not be used to fit a model. Use smoothed data to identify a model.

See "Filtering Data" in the MATLAB Data Analysis documentation for more information on smoothing and filtering.

Summarizing Data

Note This section continues the data analysis from "Preprocessing Data" on page 5-3.

MATLAB includes many functions for summarizing the overall location, scale, and shape of a data sample.

One of the advantages of working in MATLAB is that functions operate on entire arrays of data, not just on single scalar values. The functions are said to be *vectorized*. Vectorization allows for both efficient problem formulation, using array-based data, and efficient computation, using vectorized statistical functions.

- "Measures of Location" on page 5-10
- "Measures of Scale" on page 5-11
- "Shape of a Distribution" on page 5-11

Measures of Location

Summarize the location of a data sample by finding a "typical" value. Common measures of location or "central tendency" are computed by the MATLAB functions mean, median, and mode:

```
x1 = mean(count)
x1 =
   32.0000   46.5417   65.5833

x2 = median(count)
x2 =
   23.5000   36.0000   39.0000

x3 = mode(count)
x3 =
    11    9    9
```

Like all of the statistical functions in MATLAB, the functions above summarize data across observations (rows) while preserving variables (columns). The functions compute the location of the data at each of the three intersections in a single call.

Measures of Scale

There are many ways to measure the scale or "dispersion" of a data sample. The MATLAB functions max, min, std, and var compute some common measures:

```
dx1 = max(count)-min(count)
dx1 =
   107   136   250

dx2 = std(count)
dx2 =
   25.3703   41.4057   68.0281

dx3 = var(count)
dx3 =
  1.0e+003 *
    0.6437    1.7144    4.6278
```

Like all of the statistical functions in MATLAB, the functions above summarize data across observations (rows) while preserving variables (columns). The functions compute the scale of the data at each of the three intersections in a single call.

Shape of a Distribution

The shape of a distribution is harder to summarize than its location or scale. The MATLAB hist function plots a histogram that provides a visual summary:

```
figure
hist(count)
legend('Intersection 1',...
       'Intersection 2',...
       'Intersection 3')
```

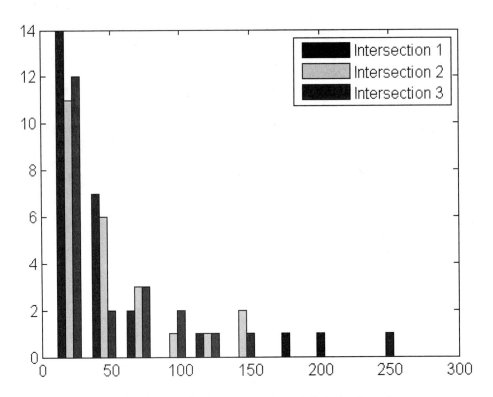

Parametric models give analytic summaries of distribution shapes. Exponential distributions, with parameter mu given by the data mean, are a good choice for the traffic data:

```
c1 = count(:,1); % Data at intersection 1
[bin_counts,bin_locations] = hist(c1);
bin_width = bin_locations(2) - bin_locations(1);
hist_area = (bin_width)*(sum(bin_counts));

figure
hist(c1)
hold on

mu1 = mean(c1);
exp_pdf = @(t)(1/mu1)*exp(-t/mu1); % Integrates
                                   % to 1

t = 0:150;
```

```
y = exp_pdf(t);
plot(t,(hist_area)*y,'r','LineWidth',2)
legend('Distribution','Exponential Fit')
```

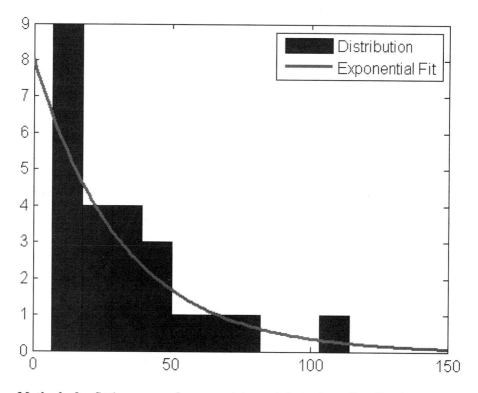

Methods for fitting general parametric models to data distributions are
beyond the scope of this Getting Started guide. Functions for computing
maximum likelihood estimates of distribution parameters are available in
Statistics Toolbox.

See "Descriptive Statistics" in the MATLAB Data Analysis documentation for
more information on summarizing data samples.

Visualizing Data

Note This section continues the data analysis from "Summarizing Data" on page 5-10.

MATLAB provides many plots for visualizing data patterns and trends. Histograms and time-series plots of the traffic data are described in the sections on "Preprocessing Data" on page 5-3 and "Summarizing Data" on page 5-10. Scatter plots, described in this section, help to visualize relationships among the traffic data at different intersections.

- "2-D Scatter Plots" on page 5-14
- "3-D Scatter Plots" on page 5-16
- "Scatter Plot Arrays" on page 5-18

2-D Scatter Plots

A 2-D scatter plot, created with the MATLAB scatter function, shows the relationship between the traffic volume at the first two intersections:

```
c1 = count(:,1); % Data at intersection 1
c2 = count(:,2); % Data at intersection 2

figure
scatter(c1,c2,'filled')
xlabel('Intersection 1')
ylabel('Intersection 2')
```

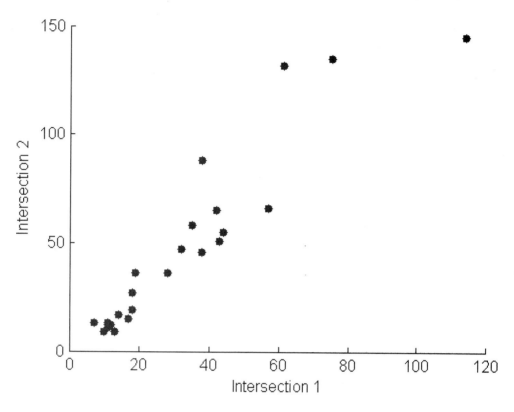

The strength of the linear relationship between the two variables (how tightly
the data lies along a least-squares line through the scatter) is measured by
the *covariance*, computed by the MATLAB cov function:

```
C12 = cov([c1 c2])
C12 =
   1.0e+003 *
      0.6437     0.9802
      0.9802     1.7144
```

The results are displayed in a symmetric square matrix, with the covariance
of the i th and j th variables in the (i, j)th position. The i th diagonal element
is the variance of the i th variable.

Covariances have the disadvantage of depending on the units used to measure
the individual variables. They are often divided by the standard deviations

of the variables to normalize values between +1 and −1. The results are *correlation coefficients*, computed by the MATLAB corrcoef function:

```
R12 = corrcoef([c1 c2])
R12 =
    1.0000    0.9331
    0.9331    1.0000

r12 = R12(1,2) % Correlation coefficient
r12 =
    0.9331

r12sq = r12^2 % Coefficient of determination
r12sq =
    0.8707
```

Because it is normalized, the value of the correlation coefficient is readily comparable to values for other pairs of intersections. Its square, the *coefficient of determination*, is the variance about the least-squares line divided by the variance about the mean. That is, it is the proportion of variation in the response (in this case, the traffic volume at intersection 2) that is eliminated or non-causally "explained" by a least-squares line through the scatter.

3-D Scatter Plots

A 3-D scatter plot, created with the MATLAB scatter3 function, shows the relationship between the traffic volume at all three intersections:

```
figure
scatter3(c1,c2,c3,'filled')
xlabel('Intersection 1')
ylabel('Intersection 2')
zlabel('Intersection 3')
```

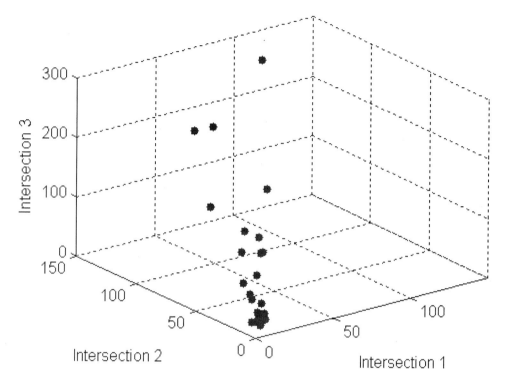

The strength of the linear relationship among the variables in the 3-D scatter is measured by computing eigenvalues of the covariance matrix with the MATLAB eig function:

```
vars = eig(cov([c1 c2 c3]))
vars =
  1.0e+003 *
    0.0442
    0.1118
    6.8300

explained = max(vars)/sum(vars)
explained =
    0.9777
```

The eigenvalues are the variances along the *principal components* of the data. The variable explained measures the proportion of variation "explained" by the first principal component, along the axis of the data. Unlike the coefficient of determination for 2-D scatters, this measure does distinguish predictor and response variables.

Scatter Plot Arrays

Use the MATLAB `plotmatrix` function to make comparisons of the relationships between multiple pairs of intersections:

```
figure
plotmatrix(count)
```

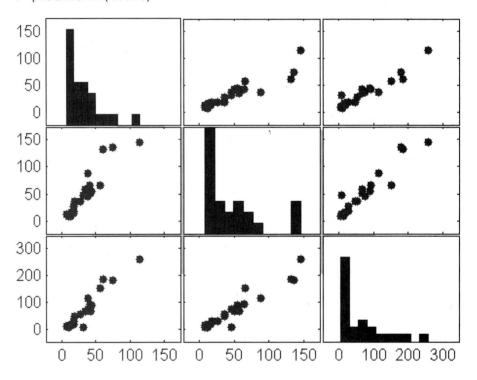

The plot in the (i, j)th position of the array is a scatter with the i th variable on the vertical axis and the j th variable on the horizontal axis. The plot in the i th diagonal position is a histogram of the i th variable.

See "Plotting Data" in the MATLAB Data Analysis documentation for more information on statistical visualization.

Modeling Data

Note This section continues the data analysis from "Visualizing Data" on page 5-14.

Parametric models translate an understanding of data relationships into analytic tools with predictive power. Polynomial and sinusoidal models are simple choices for the up and down trends in the traffic data.

- "Polynomial Regression" on page 5-19
- "General Linear Regression" on page 5-20

Polynomial Regression

Use the MATLAB polyfit function to estimate coefficients of polynomial models, then use the MATLAB polyval function to evaluate the model at arbitrary values of the predictor.

The following code fits the traffic data at the third intersection with a polynomial model of degree six:

```
c3 = count(:,3); % Data at intersection 3
tdata = (1:24)';
p_coeffs = polyfit(tdata,c3,6);

figure
plot(c3,'o-')
hold on
tfit = (1:0.01:24)';
yfit = polyval(p_coeffs,tfit);
plot(tfit,yfit,'r-','LineWidth',2)
legend('Data','Polynomial Fit','Location','NW')
```

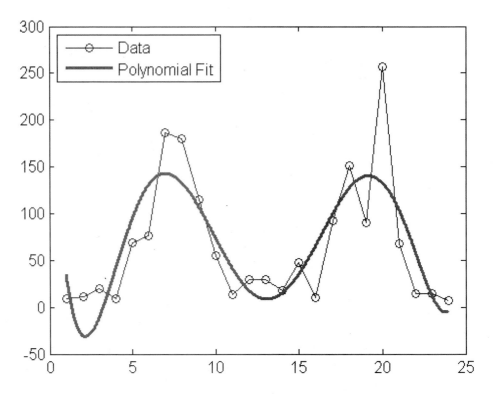

The model has the advantage of being simple while following the up-and-down trend. The accuracy of its predictive power, however, is questionable, especially at the ends of the data.

General Linear Regression

Assuming that the data are periodic with a 12-hour period and a peak around hour 7, it is reasonable to fit a sinusoidal model of the form:

$$y = a + b\cos((2\pi/12)(t - 7))$$

The coefficients a and b appear linearly. Use the MATLAB mldivide (backslash) operator to fit general linear models:

```
c3 = count(:,3); % Data at intersection 3
tdata = (1:24)';
```

```
X = [ones(size(tdata)) cos((2*pi/12)*(tdata-7))];
s_coeffs = X\c3;

figure
plot(c3,'o-')
hold on
tfit = (1:0.01:24)';
yfit = [ones(size(tfit)) cos((2*pi/12)*(tfit-7))]*s_coeffs;
plot(tfit,yfit,'r-','LineWidth',2)
legend('Data','Sinusoidal Fit','Location','NW')
```

Use the MATLAB lscov function to compute statistics on the fit, such as estimated standard errors of the coefficients and the mean squared error:

```
[s_coeffs,stdx,mse] = lscov(X,c3)
s_coeffs =
   65.5833
```

```
    73.2819
stdx =
    8.9185
   12.6127
mse =
  1.9090e+003
```

Check the assumption of a 12-hour period in the data with a *periodogram*, computed using the MATLAB fft function:

```
Fs = 1; % Sample frequency (per hour)
n = length(c3); % Window length
Y = fft(c3); % DFT of data
f = (0:n-1)*(Fs/n); % Frequency range
P = Y.*conj(Y)/n; % Power of the DFT

figure
plot(f,P)
xlabel('Frequency')
ylabel('Power')

predicted_f = 1/12
predicted_f =
    0.0833
```

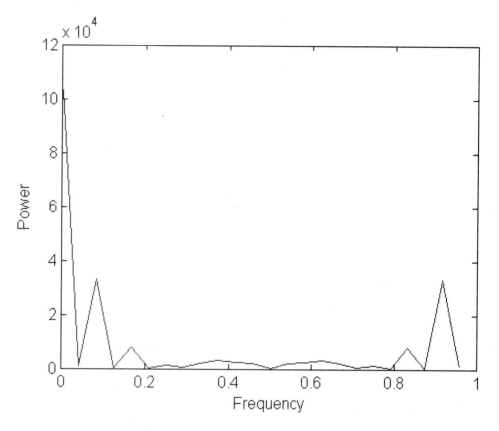

The peak near 0.0833 supports the assumption, although it occurs at a slightly higher frequency. The model can be adjusted accordingly.

See "Linear Regression Analysis" and "Fourier Analysis" in the MATLAB Data Analysis documentation for more information on data modeling.

Creating Graphical User Interfaces

What Is GUIDE?

GUIDE, the MATLAB graphical user interface development environment, provides a set of tools for creating graphical user interfaces (GUIs). These tools greatly simplify the process of designing and building GUIs. You can use the GUIDE tools to

- Lay out the GUI.

  Using the GUIDE Layout Editor, you can lay out a GUI easily by clicking and dragging GUI components—such as panels, buttons, text fields, sliders, menus, and so on—into the layout area. GUIDE stores the GUI layout in a FIG-file.

- Program the GUI.

  GUIDE automatically generates an M-file that controls how the GUI operates. The M-file initializes the GUI and contains a framework for the most commonly used callbacks for each component—the commands that execute when a user clicks a GUI component. Using the M-file editor, you can add code to the callbacks to perform the functions you want.

Note You can also create GUIs programmatically. For information on how to get started, see "Creating a Simple GUI Programmatically" in the MATLAB Creating Graphical User interfaces documentation.

Laying Out a GUI

- "Starting GUIDE" on page 6-3
- "The Layout Editor" on page 6-3

Starting GUIDE

Start GUIDE by typing guide at the MATLAB command prompt. This displays the GUIDE Quick Start dialog box, as shown in the following figure.

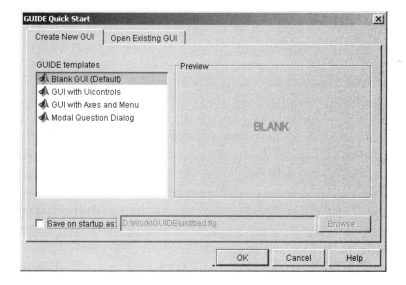

From the GUIDE Quick Start dialog box, you can

- Create a new GUI from one of the GUIDE templates—prebuilt GUIs that you can modify for your own purposes.
- Open an existing GUI.

The Layout Editor

When you open a GUI in GUIDE, it is displayed in the Layout Editor, which is the control panel for all of the GUIDE tools. The following figure shows the Layout Editor with a blank GUI template.

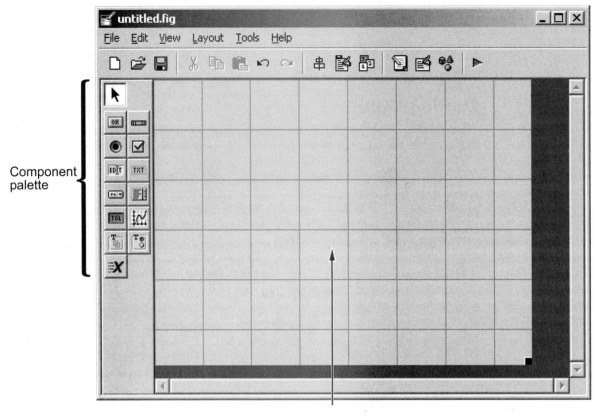

Layout Area

You can lay out your GUI by dragging components, such as panels, push buttons, pop-up menus, or axes, from the component palette, at the left side of the Layout Editor, into the layout area. For example, if you drag a push button into the layout area, it appears as in the following figure.

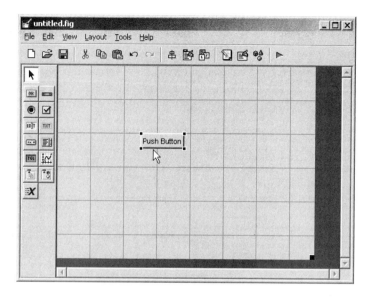

You can also use the Layout Editor to create menus and set basic properties of the GUI components.

To get started using the Layout Editor and setting property values, see "Creating a Simple GUI with GUIDE" in the MATLAB Creating Graphical User Interfaces documentation.

Programming a GUI

After laying out the GUI and setting component properties, the next step is to program the GUI. You program the GUI by coding one or more callbacks for each of its components. Callbacks are functions that execute in response to some action by the user. A typical action is clicking a push button.

A GUI's callbacks are found in an M-file that GUIDE generates automatically. GUIDE adds templates for the most commonly used callbacks to this M-file, but you may want to add others. Use the M-file Editor to edit this file.

The following figure shows the Callback template for a push button.

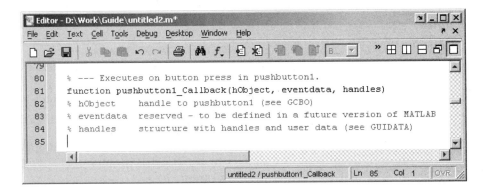

To learn more about programming a GUI, see "Creating a Simple GUI with GUIDE" in the MATLAB Creating GUIs documentation.

Desktop Tools and Development Environment

Desktop Overview

- "Introduction to the Desktop" on page 7-2
- "Arranging the Desktop" on page 7-4
- "Start Button" on page 7-4

Introduction to the Desktop

Use desktop tools to manage your work in MATLAB. You can also use MATLAB functions to perform the equivalent of most of the features found in the desktop tools.

The following illustration shows the default configuration of the MATLAB desktop. You can modify the setup to meet your needs.

Menus change, depending on the tool you are using.

Enter MATLAB statements at the prompt.

View or change the current directory.

Move or resize the Command Window.

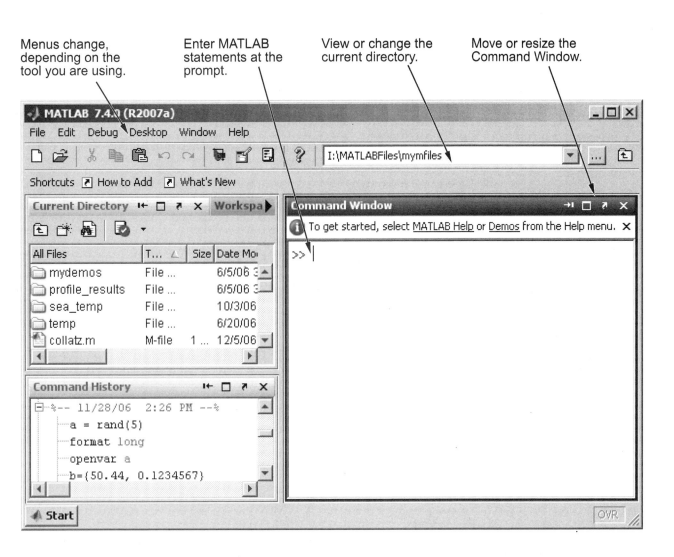

For More Information For an overview of the desktop tools, watch the video tutorials, accessible by typing demo matlab desktop (requires an Internet connection). For complete details, see the MATLAB Desktop Tools and Development Environment documentation.

Arranging the Desktop

These are some common ways to customize the desktop:

- Show or hide desktop tools via the **Desktop** menu.

- Resize any tool by dragging one of its edges.

- Move a tool outside of the desktop by clicking the undock button ⬚ in the tool's title bar.

- Reposition a tool within the desktop by dragging its title bar to the new location. Tools can occupy the same position, as shown for the Current Directory and Workspace browser in the preceding illustration, in which case, you access a tool via its name in the title bar.

- Maximize or minimize (temporarily hide) a tool within the desktop via the **Desktop** menu.

- Change fonts and other options by using **File > Preferences**.

Start Button

The MATLAB **Start** button provides easy access to tools, demos, shortcuts, and documentation. Click the **Start** button to see the options.

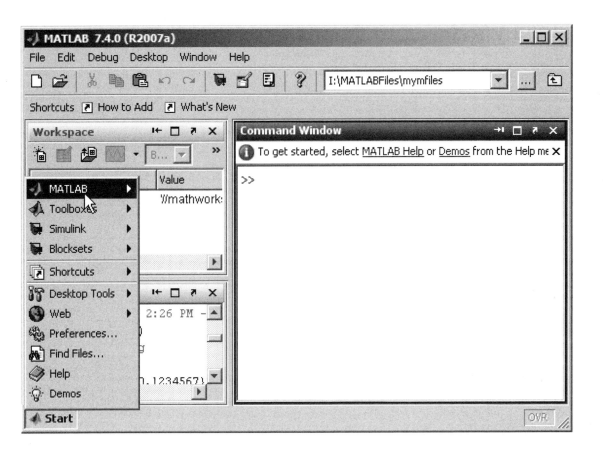

For More Information See "Desktop" in the MATLAB Desktop Tools and
Development Environment documentation.

Command Window and Command History

- "Command Window" on page 7-6
- "Command History" on page 7-7

Command Window

Use the Command Window to enter variables and to run functions and M-file scripts.

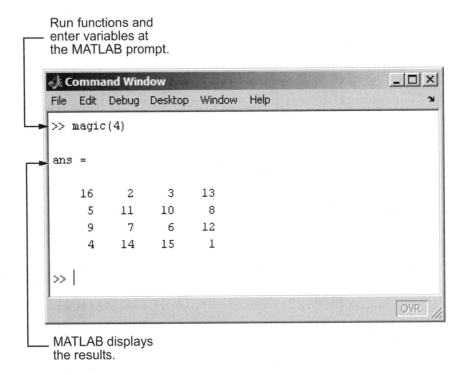

Run functions and enter variables at the MATLAB prompt.

MATLAB displays the results.

Press the up arrow key ↑ to recall a statement you previously typed. Edit the statement as needed and then press **Enter** to run it. For more information about entering statements in the Command Window, see "Controlling Command Window Input and Output" on page 2-29.

For More Information See "Running Functions — Command Window and History" in the MATLAB Desktop Tools and Development Environment documentation for complete details.

Command History

Statements you enter in the Command Window are logged in the Command History. From the Command History, you can view and search for previously run statements, as well as copy and execute selected statements. You can also create an M-file from selected statements.

Timestamp marks the start of each session.

Select one or more entries and right-click to copy, evaluate, or create an M-file from the selection.

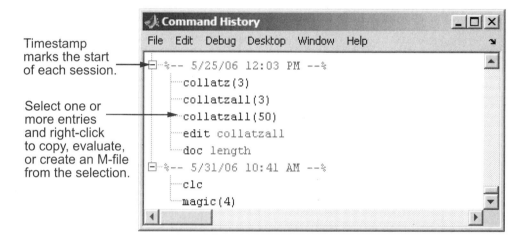

To save the input and output from a MATLAB session to a file, use the diary function.

For More Information See "Command History" in the MATLAB Desktop Tools and Development Environment documentation, and the reference page for the diary function.

Help Browser

Use the Help browser to search for and view documentation and demos for all your MathWorks products. The Help browser is an HTML viewer integrated into the MATLAB desktop.

To open the Help browser, click the Help button ❓ in the desktop toolbar.

The Help browser consists of two panes, the **Help Navigator**, which you use to find information, and the display pane, where you view the information. These are the key features:

- **Search for** field — Look for specific words in the documentation and demos. You can

    - Specify an exact phrase by enclosing words in double quotation marks, such as `"word1 word2"`

    - Use a wildcard symbol (`*`) in place of letters, such as `wo*d1`

    - Include Boolean operators between words, such as `word1 NOT word2`

- **Contents** tab — View the titles and tables of contents of the documentation. By default, the contents synchronizes to the displayed page. If you get to a page from a search or by following a link, click the **Contents** tab if you want to see the context within the overall documentation for the page you are viewing.

- **Index** tab — Find specific index entries (selected keywords) in the documentation.

- **Search Results** tab — Displays results from **Search for**, separating the results in Documentation from the results in Demos.

- **Demos** tab — View and run demonstrations for your MathWorks products. Demos include code that you can use as a basis for creating your own M-files.

While viewing the documentation, you can

- Browse to other pages — Use the arrows at the tops and bottoms of the pages to move through the document, or use the back and forward buttons in the toolbar to go to previously viewed pages.

- Bookmark pages — Use the **Favorites** menu.
- Print a page — Click the print button in the toolbar.
- Find a term in the page — Click the find icon 🔍 in the toolbar.
- Copy or evaluate a selection — Select text, such as code from an example, then right-click and use a context menu item to copy the selection or evaluate (run) it.

Tabs in the **Help Navigator** pane provide different ways to find information.

Click the Close box to hide the pane.

Drag the separator bar to adjust the width of the panes.

View documentation in the display pane.

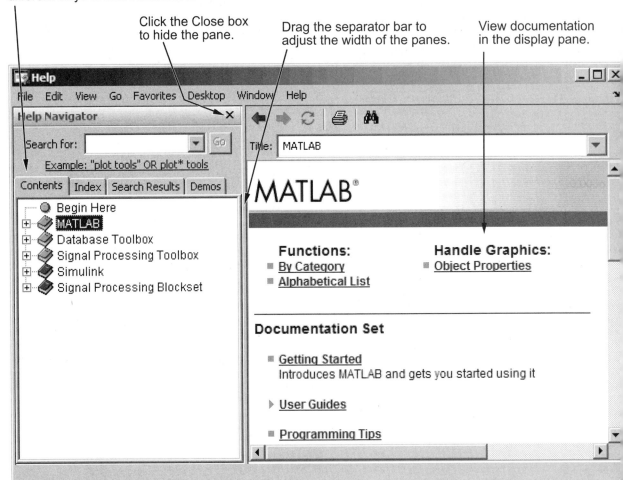

Other Forms of Help

In addition to the Help browser, you can use help functions. To get help for a specific function, use the doc function. For example, doc format displays documentation for the format function in the Help browser.

To see a briefer form of the documentation for a function, type `help` followed by the function name. The resulting help text appears in the Command Window. It shows function names in all capital letters to distinguish them from the surrounding text. When you use the function names, type them in lowercase or they will not run. Some functions actually consist of both uppercase and lowercase letters, and the help text clearly indicates that. For those functions, match the case used in the `help` function.

Other means for getting help include contacting Technical Support (`www.mathworks.com/support`) and participating in the Usenet newsgroup for MATLAB users, `comp.soft-sys.matlab`.

For More Information See "Help for Using MATLAB" in the MATLAB Desktop Tools and Development Environment documentation, and the reference pages for the `doc` and `help` functions.

Current Directory Browser and Search Path

MATLAB file operations use the current directory and the search path as reference points. Any file you want to run must either be in the current directory or on the search path.

- "Current Directory" on page 7-12
- "Search Path" on page 7-13

Current Directory

A quick way to view or change the current directory is by using the current directory field in the desktop toolbar, shown here.

To search for, view, open, and make changes to MATLAB related directories and files, use the MATLAB Current Directory browser. Alternatively, you can use the functions dir, cd, and delete. Use "Directory Reports in Current Directory Browser" to help you tune and manage M-files.

Change the directory here.
This field only appears here when
the Current Directory browser is
undocked from the desktop.

Search for files
and content
within text files.

Access directory
reports.

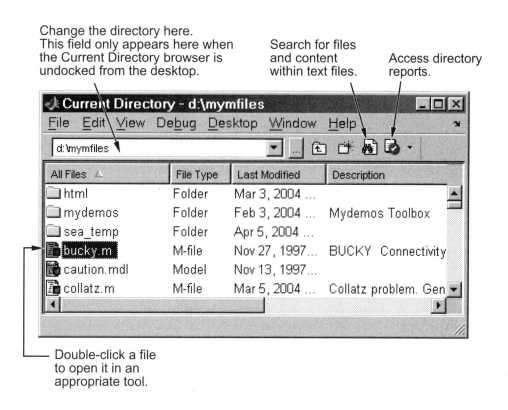

Double-click a file
to open it in an
appropriate tool.

For More Information See "File Management Operations" in the MATLAB
Desktop Tools and Development Environment documentation, and the
reference pages for the dir, cd, and delete functions.

Search Path

MATLAB uses a *search path* to find M-files and other MATLAB related files,
which are organized in directories on your file system. Any file you want to
run in MATLAB must reside in the current directory or in a directory that is
on the search path. When you create M-files and related files for MATLAB,
add the directories in which they are located to the MATLAB search path. By
default, the files supplied with MATLAB and other MathWorks products are
included in the search path.

To see which directories are on the search path or to change the search path, select **File > Set Path** and use the resulting Set Path dialog box. Alternatively, you can use the path function to view the search path, addpath to add directories to the path, and rmpath to remove directories from the path.

For More Information See "Search Path" in the MATLAB Desktop Tools and Development Environment documentation, and the reference pages for the path, addpath, and rmpath functions.

Workspace Browser and Array Editor

- "Workspace Browser" on page 7-15
- "Array Editor" on page 7-16

Workspace Browser

The MATLAB workspace consists of the set of variables (named arrays) built up during a MATLAB session and stored in memory. You add variables to the workspace by using functions, running M-files, and loading saved workspaces.

To view the workspace and information about each variable, use the Workspace browser, or use the functions who and whos.

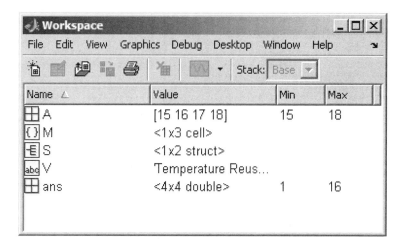

To delete variables from the workspace, select the variables and select **Edit > Delete**. Alternatively, use the clear function.

The workspace is not maintained after you end the MATLAB session. To save the workspace to a file that can be read during a later MATLAB session, select **File > Save**, or use the save function. This saves the workspace to a binary file called a MAT-file, which has a .mat extension. You can use options to save to different formats. To read in a MAT-file, select **File > Import Data**, or use the load function.

For More Information See "MATLAB Workspace" in the MATLAB Desktop Tools and Development Environment documentation, and the reference pages for the who, clear, save, and load functions.

Array Editor

Double-click a variable in the Workspace browser, or use openvar variablename, to see it in the Array Editor. Use the Array Editor to view and edit a visual representation of variables in the workspace.

View and change values of array elements.

Arrange the display of array documents.

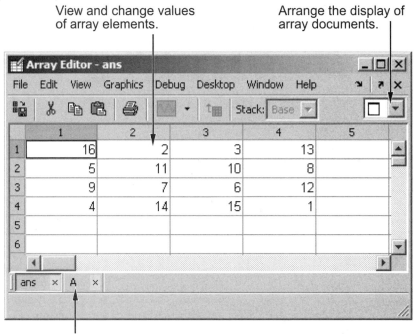

Use the document bar to view other variables you have open in the Array Editor.

For More Information See "Viewing and Editing Workspace Variables with the Array Editor" in the MATLAB Desktop Tools and Development Environment documentation, and the reference page for the openvar function.

Editor/Debugger

Use the Editor/Debugger to create and debug M-files, which are programs you write to run MATLAB functions. The Editor/Debugger provides a graphical user interface for text editing, as well as for M-file debugging. To create or edit an M-file use **File > New** or **File > Open**, or use the edit function.

Set breakpoints where you want execution to pause so you can examine the variables.

Comment selected lines and specify the indenting style using the **Text** menu.

Arrange the display of documents in the Editor/Debugger.

M-lint automatic code analyzer.

Find and replace text.

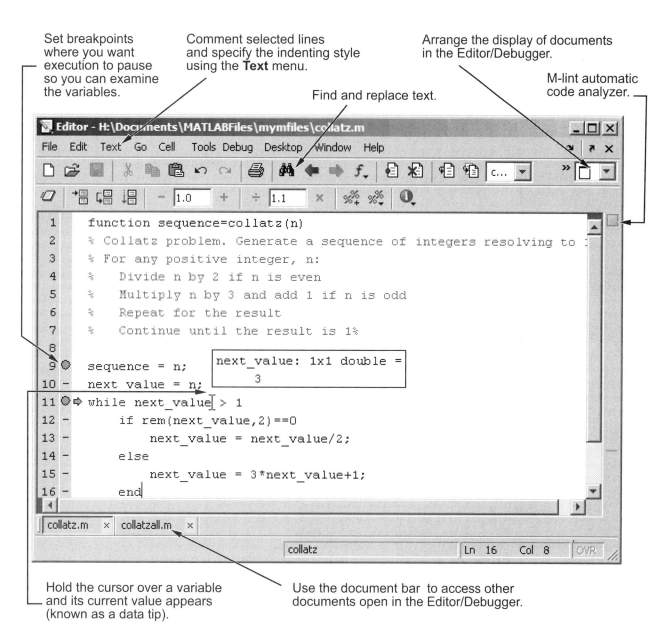

```matlab
1    function sequence=collatz(n)
2    % Collatz problem. Generate a sequence of integers resolving to
3    % For any positive integer, n:
4    %    Divide n by 2 if n is even
5    %    Multiply n by 3 and add 1 if n is odd
6    %    Repeat for the result
7    %    Continue until the result is 1%
8
9    sequence = n;
10   next value = n;
11   while next_value > 1
12       if rem(next_value,2)==0
13           next_value = next_value/2;
14       else
15           next_value = 3*next_value+1;
16       end
```

next_value: 1x1 double =
3

collatz.m   ×   collatzall.m   ×

collatz   Ln 16   Col 8   OVR

Hold the cursor over a variable and its current value appears (known as a data tip).

Use the document bar to access other documents open in the Editor/Debugger.

You can use any text editor to create M-files, such as Emacs. Use preferences (accessible from the desktop **File** menu) to specify that editor as the default.

If you use another editor, you can still use the MATLAB Editor/Debugger for debugging, or you can use debugging functions, such as dbstop, which sets a breakpoint.

If you just need to view the contents of an M-file, you can display the contents in the Command Window using the type function.

Use the M-Lint automatic code analyzer to help you identify problems and potential improvements in your code. For details, see "M-Lint Code Check and Profiler Reports" on page 7-21.

You can evaluate your code in sections, called cells, and can publish your code, including results, to popular output formats like HTML. For more information, see "Using Cells for Rapid Code Iteration and Publishing Results" in the MATLAB Desktop Tools and Development Environment documentation.

For More Information See "Editing and Debugging M-Files" in the MATLAB Desktop Tools and Development Environment documentation, and the function reference pages for edit, type, and debug.

M-Lint Code Check and Profiler Reports

MATLAB provides tools to help you manage and improve your M-files, including the M-Lint Code Check and Profiler Reports.

- "M-Lint Code Check Report" on page 7-21
- "Profiler" on page 7-24

M-Lint Code Check Report

The M-Lint Code Check Report displays potential errors and problems, as well as opportunities for improvement in your M-files. The term *lint* is used by similar tools in other programming languages such as C.

Access the M-Lint Code Check Report and other directory reports from the Current Directory browser. You run a report for all files in the current directory.

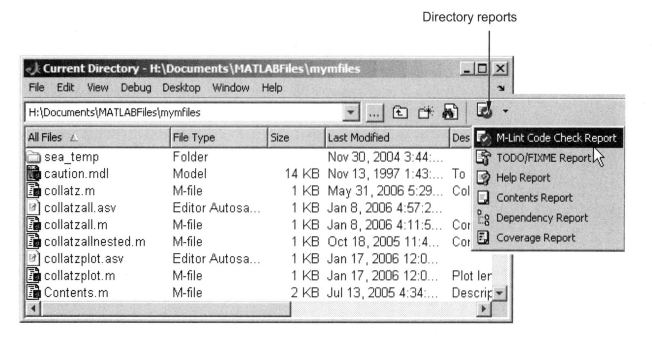

In MATLAB, the M-Lint Code Check Report displays a message for each line of an M-file it determines might be improved. For example, a common M-Lint message is that a variable is defined but never used in the M-file.

The report displays a line number and message for
each potential problem or improvement opportunity.

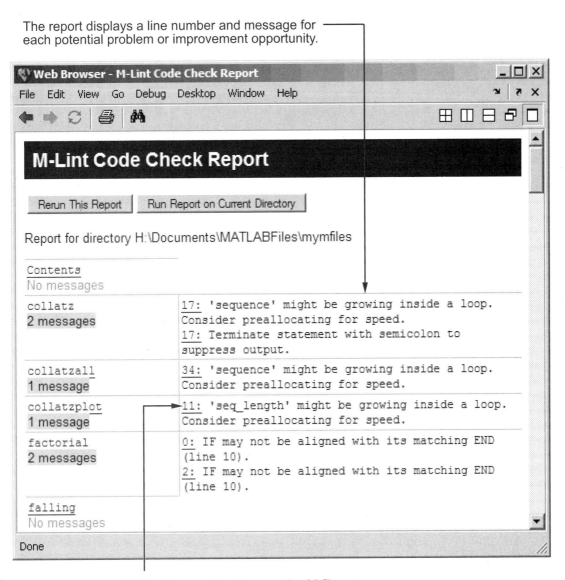

Click a line number to open the M-file
in the Editor/Debugger at that line.

Alternatively, you can use automatic M-Lint code checking to view M-Lint messages while you work on a file in the Editor/Debugger. You can also use the mlint function to get results for a single M-file.

For More Information See "Tuning and Managing M-Files" and "M-Lint Code Analyzer" in the MATLAB Desktop Tools and Development Environment documentation, and the reference page for the mlint function.

Profiler

MATLAB includes the Profiler to help you improve the performance of your M-files. Run a MATLAB statement or an M-file in the Profiler and it produces a report of where the time is being spent. Access the Profiler from the **Desktop** menu, or use the profile function.

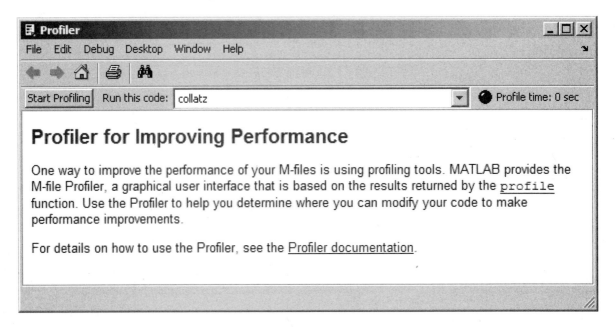

For More Information See "Tuning and Managing M-Files" in the MATLAB Desktop Tools and Development Environment documentation, and the reference page for the `profile` function.

Other Development Environment Features

Additional development environment features include

- Source Control — Access your source control system from within MATLAB.

- Publishing Results — Use the Editor/Debugger's cell features to publish M-files and results to popular output formats including HTML and Microsoft Word. You can also use MATLAB Notebook to access MATLAB functions from within Microsoft Word.

For More Information See "Source Control Interface" and "Publishing Results" in the MATLAB Desktop Tools and Development Environment documentation.

Index